About the Author

I am a native Oklahoman and have always maintained a very keen interest in the natural vegetation of our state. The eastern, rural hills of Grady County provided the environment for my childhood and early teens until high school graduation at Bradley. A Bachelor of Science degree was earned at East Central University with a major in the biological sciences. A Master of Science degree was earned at Oklahoma University with a botany major. The Ph. D. degree was earned at Oklahoma State University with a botany major. Work toward completion of each degree provided good opportunities for field work in an area of botany that I found most challenging — native plant identification.

Prior to retirement, in 1982, I was privileged to be a classroom teacher for a period of forty-five years. During most of that time I taught botany courses at East Central University and Cameron University.

My wife, the former Pearl Hayes, is also a native Oklahoman. She is now retired after serving as a librarian in senior high school and university libraries. We recently observed our fiftieth wedding anniversary. Our only daughter, Judy, is a Texas resident where she too is a teacher. Our only grandson, Allen, is a student at Southwest Texas University.

Two books, of which I am the author, were published and are distributed by the University of Oklahoma Press. They are *Roadside Wild Fruits of Oklahoma* and *Roadside Trees and Shrubs of Oklahoma*. I do not distribute these two books except on a single book basis to individuals.

Four books, of which I am the author, were published by contract and are available in bookstores or from the address provided below. In addition to the present volume, *Oklahoma Wildflowers*, they include *A Study of Flowering Plants, Roadside Flowers of Oklahoma*, vol. 1, and *Roadside Flowers of Oklahoma*, vol. 2.

Dr. Doyle McCoy
700 S.W. 102
Oklahoma City, Oklahoma 73139
Ph. (405) 691-8928

Contents

Page

Oklahoma Wildflowers

Doyle McCoy, Ph.D.

ISBN 0-9619985-1-2

To my wife, Pearl H. McCoy, whose constant support and encouragement helped to make this publication possible.

Introduction and Acknowledgments

This book has grown out of my lifetime interest in the wildflowers of Oklahoma. It is, in reality, another in a series of books that deal with identification, understanding and enjoyment of our state's natural vegetation. Among the many qualities of our woodlands, meadows, stream-banks, mountains and prairies, the wildflowers are, perhaps, most striking. Even the most casual observer is impressed with the beauty and diversity of their sparkling array of colors. They blossom in successive waves throughout the growing season, providing a fresh panorama each time we visit, even the same area, from time to time.

Included for each species listed in this book are a description, one or more color photographs, distribution information, full scientific name, one or more common names, family names — scientific and common — and flowering dates. It was necessary to spend considerable time traveling over the state in order to get the best photographs possible and to observe and record other structures or features. These were pleasant experiences for this botanist since I could anticipate some pleasant surprises on each excursion.

In order to provide a book with more adaptability to field use, certain features have been added which are not present in my earlier plant guides. The one with which I am most pleased is the inclusion of two separate plates for each of many of the species shown. There is a close-up view for every species covered. This is essential, in most cases, for satisfactory identification. However, to show the entire plant, cluster of plants or large communities, a number of extra plates are included. Also included in this format is the grouping of the plates according to color shades. This provides aesthetic advantages, and more important, improves the facility with which one may match a photo with a field specimen.

I am indebted to many people for assistance in preparing this book. Special encouragement has come from the Garden Clubs of Oklahoma; the Oklahoma Academy of Science; the Oklahoma Ornithological Society; the Oklahoma Horticultural Society; fellow botanists of colleges and universities; public school teachers; and landowners who shared their acreages with me. Two very good slide collections were made available to me and some photos from each of these are used in this book. I am very grateful to Mr. W. Harvey Faust, now deceased, and to the Public Affairs Division of the Oklahoma Department of Transportation for the use of their nice photographs.

Proboscidea louisianica
Devil's Claw
(Proboscis Flower, Ram's Horn,
Unicorn Plant, Elephant's Trunk,
Double Claw)
Martyniaceae — Unicorn Family

The stems are much branched, spreading, may become prostrate, and 1-3 feet long. The leaf blades are almost circular but slightly heart-shaped, smooth on the edges, and 3-12 inches long. The flowers are in racemes at the stem tips. Each flower is yellowish or white with purplish or yellow dots within, tubular, five-lobed, slightly irregular, and 1-2 inches long. The fruits are strongly curved, 4-6 inches long and with a pointed beak that splits when mature, forming a pair of claws. They are fairly common in Western Oklahoma, in moist sandy fields. July - September.

Asclepias stenophylla
Narrow-leaved Milkweed
Asclepiadaceae — Milkweed Family

The stems are usually in small groups, erect and 1-2 feet tall. The leaves are paired at the nodes, very slender and 2-5 inches long. Flowers are in 10-15 flowered umbels which are numerous. The five petal segments are oblong and greenish. The fruiting follicles are slender, erect and about three inches long. They grow on dry plains of the western half of our state. June - September.

Asclepias latifolia
Broad-leaved Milkweed
Asclepiadaceae — Milkweed Family

These are stout-stemmed plants that grow in clusters from perennial roots, and are 2-2½ feet tall. The leaves are without petioles, 4-6 inches long, and nearly as wide. The flowers are in umbels on short peduncles in the upper leaf axes. Each flower is greenish, about a fourth inch wide, and five-parted. The follicle fruits are oval, 2-3 inches long and about an inch thick. They are widely distributed on dry plains. July -September.

Asclepias asperula, var. *decumbens*
Antelope Horns
(Creeping Milkweed)
Asclepiadaceae — Milkweed Family

The stems are partly decumbent or spreading, minutely hairy or smooth and 1-2 feet long. The leaves are narrowly lanceolate and 3-7 inches long. The flowers are many in solitary umbrella-like clusters with individual flower stalks ½-1 inch long. Each flower is greenish with a purplish hood. The fruiting pods are nearly erect and 3-4 inches long. They are found in dry soils of prairies, mostly western. April - June.

Asclepias viridis
Green Milkweed
(Oblong-leaved Milkweed)
Asclepiadaceae — Milkweed Family

The stems are simple, erect, and 1-2 feet tall. Their leaves are oblong-ovate, short-petioled, 2-5 inches long, and ½-2 inches wide. The flowers are in terminal umbels. Each flower is greenish, five-parted, and about an inch broad. The follicle fruits are 2-3 inches long and about a half inch thick. They are widely distributed, especially in the eastern half of the state, and prefer prairie habitats. May - July.

Monarda punctata
Horse Mint
Labiatae — Mint Family

Their stems are very obviously square, hairy, highly branched and 2-3 feet high. The leaves are narrow, toothed and 1-3 inches long. The flowers are in 1-4 compact masses at the upper part of each stem. Each flower is strongly 2-lipped, tubular and yellow with purple spots. They occur with high frequency in dry sandy fields of the western half of Oklahoma. July - October.

Vernonia missurica
Prairie Ironweed
Compositae — Composite Family

The stems are stout and 2-4 feet tall. The leaves are lanceolate to narrowly oblong, finely toothed and 3-6 inches long. The flowering heads are rather compactly clustered at the stem tips. They are pink to purple in color with each head bearing 30-60 tiny flowers. These ironweeds grow in abandoned fields and prairie pastures. August -October.

Gaillardia suavis
Rayless Gaillardia
Compositae — Composite Family

The stems are unbranched, except occasionally at the base, and 1-2 feet tall. The leaves are basal only, divided into lobes that are variously notched, and 2-6 inches long. The heads are about an inch broad and globose. Rays are nearly always absent. The flowers are tubular, purplish-red, regular, and five-toothed. They frequently occur in dry habitats in the eastern two-thirds of the state. April - June.

Sphaeralcea coccinea
False Mallow
(Globe Mallow, Moss Rose)
Malvaceae — Mallow Family

The stems are mostly erect, freely branched, silvery-hairy and 6-12 inches high. The leaves are ½-2 inches wide, about the same length and divided to form narrow, irregular leaflets. The flowers are reddish-orange, ½-¾ inch broad and in dense clusters at the stem tips. They are fairly numerous in western Oklahoma. May - August.

Aesculus Pavia
Red Buckeye
(Little Buckeye, Fish Poison)
Hippocastanaceae — Buckeye Family

These are small shrubs that are diffusely branched and reach a height of 3-6 feet. The flowers are in racemes that are 6-12 inches long. Each flower is tubular, red, irregular in form and 1-1½ inches long. They grow in low meadows of our southeastern counties. April - June.

Castilleja purpurea, forma *corallina*
Coral Paint Brush
Scrophulariaceae — Figwort Family

These plants are 1-2 feet tall and very
hairy. The flowers are in clusters at
the stem tips and are almost hidden
by coral-pink bracts. They are less
numerous than the other paint
brushes and restricted to the southern
and eastern counties. April - July.

Echinocereus Baileyi
Barrel Cactus
(Hedgehog Cereus)
Cactaceae — Cactus Family

The stems are globose to oval and 2-8 inches tall. The spines are ¼-⅓ inch long and very rigid. The flowers are pink and 1-3 inches wide. There are many petals and many stamens. Each plant may produce 1-4 flowers each year. These plants are found in rocky soils of a few southwestern counties (such as Comanche, Kiowa and Jackson). May - July.

Petalostemum purpureum
Purple Prairie Clover
(Thimble Weed, Red Tassel-flower)
Leguminosae — Legume Family

These plants branch above and reach a height of 1-3 feet. The leaves are divided into only 3-5 leaflets that are ¼-¾ inch long and less than ¹⁄₁₂ inch broad. Their flowers grow in spikes that are ½-2 inches long and almost a half inch thick. The purple flowers are about a fifth inch long. They are widely distributed on prairires and roadsides throughout Oklahoma. June - August.

Centaurea americana
**American Star Thistle
(Red Basket Thistle)**
Compositae — Composite Family

The stems are branched and 2-6 feet tall. The leaves are toothed or smooth, lanceolate, and 2-5 inches long. The flowers are in heads on long peduncles, and are 2-4 inches broad. There are no rays. All of their flowers are purple or pink, the outer ones being much larger. They are widespread on dry plains. May -August.

Spigela Marylandica
**Indian Pink
(Carolina Pink, Pink Root, Star Bloom)**
Loganiaceae — Logania Family

These plants are perennials with four-angled stems which are fairly smooth and 1-2 feet tall. Their leaves are sessile, ovate-acuminate at the apex and 2-4 inches long. The flowers are scarlet outside, yellow within and 1-2 inches long. They grow in forested uplands of McCurtain and LeFlore counties. April - June.

Asclepias tuberosa
**Butterfly Weed
(Chigger Weed, Indian Posy,
Orange Root)**
Asclepiadaceae — Milkweed Family

These are mostly unbranched plants
that grow in clusters and are 1-2 feet
tall. The leaves are without petioles,
2-6 inches long, and ⅛-1 inch wide.
The flowers are in compact umbels at
the stem tips. Each flower is bright
red, orange or yellow, five-lobed, and
about a fourth inch wide. The follicle
fruits are 4-5 inches long and about
an inch thick. They are widely
distributed and thrive in dry fields
and prairies. June - September.

Lonicera sempervirens
**Coral Honeysuckle
(Coral Vine, Woodbine, Scarlet
Honeysuckle)**
Caprifoliaceae — Honeysuckle Family

These are high-climbing vines that are
mostly smooth and evergreen. The
flowers are yellow to scarlet, tubular
and 1-1½ inches long. They grow in
low grounds or on moist slopes of
our southeastern counties. April
-September.

Gilia rubra
**Standing Cypress
(Scarlet Gilia)**
Polemoniaceae — Phlox Family

These are mostly unbranched plants
that are stout and 2-5 feet tall. The
leaf blades are finely divided into
threadlike segments that are ½-1 inch
long. The flowers are scarlet red and
in racemes at the stem tips. Each
flower is tubular, ½-1 inch long, five-
parted, and about a half inch wide at
the lobes. They grow infrequently
throughout, and are most likely seen
in open woods of hillsides. June
-August.

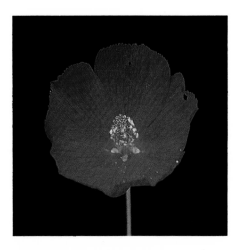

Callirhoe digitata
**Fringed Poppy Mallow
(Tall Wine Cup)**
Malvaceae — Mallow Family

These plants are 2-4 feet tall, slightly
branched and smooth or sparsely
hairy. The leaves are composed of
several segments and have long
petioles. The flowers are on long
stalks that grow from the leaf angles.
Each flower is 1-2 inches broad,
reddish-purple and has fringed
margins. They are infrequent in
Oklahoma and thrive best in rocky,
limestone soil of hillsides. April -July.

Lobelia cardinalis
**Cardinal Flower
(Red Lobelia, Red Betty, Slink
Weed)**
Campanulaceae — Bell-flower Family

The stems are rarely branched and
2-5 feet tall. The leaves are oval or
lanceolate, toothed, 2-6 inches long,
and ¼-1½ inches wide. The flowers
are in terminal racemes and
numerous. Each flower is scarlet red,
tubular, five-lobed, irregular, 1-1½
inches long, and very striking in appearance. They are infrequent and occur mostly in low, moist soils, but
are occasionally observed over most
of the state. July - September.

Callirhoe involucrata
**Wine Cup
(Cowboy Rose, Purple Poppy
Mallow)**
Malvaceae — Mallow Family

The stems are weak and highly
branched, reaching a length of 1-2
feet. The leaves have long petioles,
and blades that are 1-3 inches long,
about as broad, and deeply notched.
The flowers are on long stalks from
the leaf angles. Each flower is 1-2½
inches broad and red-purple with five
separate petals. They are widely
distributed on prairies throughout our
area. April - August.

Gaillardia pulchella
Indian Blanket
(Gaillardia, Fire Wheel, Showy
Gaillardia)
Compositae — Composite Family

This attractive little wildflower is now the official state wildflower. The measure was passed by the fortieth legislative session (1986) and signed by Governor Nigh on March 20, 1986. The stems are diffusely branched from the base and 6-15 inches tall. The leaves are oblong, deeply lobed, toothed or smooth and 1-3 inches long. The heads are few, 1-3 inches broad and on long peduncles. The 10-20 rays are red or purple at the bases, yellow toward the tips, about an inch long and three-lobed at the tips. The central

flowers are purplish-brown, tubular and five-lobed. They are widely distributed in various soils of Oklahoma. May - September.

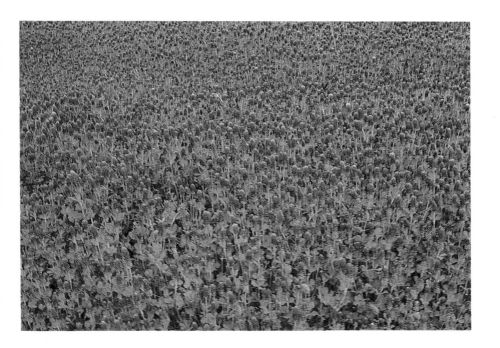

Trifolium incarnatum
Crimson Clover
(Carnation Clover, French Clover,
Italian Clover, Napoleon's Clover)
Leguminosae — Legume Family

The plants are annual, erect, soft-hairy, sparsely branched and 1-3 feet tall. The leaf blades are divided into three leaflets that are fan-like and ½-1 inch long. The flowers are in terminal heads that are 1-3 inches long. Each flower is red and ⅓-½ inch long. They are not very frequent but occur in sporadic communities throughout the eastern half of the state. May - July.

Carduus marianus (Silybum Marianum)
**Holy Thistle
(Virgin Mary's Thistle, Milk Thistle)**
Compositae — Composite Family

These plants have sturdy stems which may reach a height of 2-4 feet with little or no branching. The leaves are very numerous and large, some growing to a length of one foot and a width of one-half foot. However, the upper leaves are reduced to a much smaller size. All leaves are conspicuously streaked with white. The heads of flowers are only at the tips of stems and are reddish-purple. Bracts surrounding the flowers are very rigid, long and sharply tipped. These thistles are at the present time, limited in Oklahoma, having been observed only in Blaine County. May - July.

Carduus nutans
Queen Ann's Thistle
(Musk Thistle, Plumeless Thistle, Bank Thistle)
Compositae — Composite Family

These plants are branched, 2-4 feet tall with spiny wings on the stems. The flowering heads are on long stalks, 1-3 inches broad and purple to white. They grow in open woodlands or low meadows in mostly the northeast fourth of the state. June - October.

— 18 —

Cirsium texanum
Texas Thistle
Compositae — Composite Family

These are slender perennials with spine-tipped leaves and are 2-3 feet tall. The heads are pink to purplish, 1-2 inches broad and at the tips of long, almost leafless stalks. They grow on prairies of the western half of the state. May - September.

Cirsium altissimum
Tall Thistle
Compositae — Composite Family

The stems are stout, branched, very
leafy, and 3-10 feet tall. The leaves
are oval or oblong, whitish, spiny-
margined, toothed, and 1-8 inches
long. The heads are about two inches
broad, 1-2 inches high, on the upper
stem tips, and without rays. Each
flower is light purple, tubular, five-
lobed, and regular. They are mostly
eastern and prefer low fields or
roadsides. August - September.

Ipomoea leptophylla
Bush Morning Glory
Convolvulaceae — Morning Glory
Family

The stems are freely branched from
the base, smooth, reclining or upright
and 2-4 feet tall. The leaves are
simple, very narrow and 2-5 inches
long. The flowers are purple to pink,
bell-like and about three inches long.
These plants inhabit open areas in
dry soils that are often sandy or
gravelly. They are restricted to the
western half of our state. May - July.

Oxytropis Lambertii
Stemles Loco
(Loco Weed, Crazy Weed)
Leguminosae — Legume Family

These are silky-hairy plants with
very shortened stems. The leaves are
4-9 inches long and divided into 9-19
leaflets that are ¾-1 inch long and
up to ¼ inch broad. The flowers are
in spikes at the upper part of
peduncles that are 6-12 inches long.
The flowers are purple to yellow-
purple and about an inch long. Each
pod is ½-1 inch long, covered with
hair, and has a long curving tip.
They are widely distributed in rocky
or gravelly soils of prairies. April
-August.

Castilleja indivisa
**Indian Paint Brush
(Paint Cup)**
Scrophulariaceae — Figwort Family

These are mostly unbranched plants
that are 8-18 inches high. The leaves
are smooth-edged, 1-4 inches long,
and ⅛-¼ inch wide. The upper leaves
(in the floral area) are tipped with
bright red color. The flowers are
clustered at the stem tips, about an
inch long, irregular in form, and
almost hidden by the upper leaves
(bracts). They grow in sandy soils
and are more frequent in the western
two-thirds of Oklahoma. May - June.

Campsis radicans
Trumpet Creeper
(Trumpet Flower, Trumpet Ash,
Cow Itch, Cross Vine)
Bignoniaceae — Trumpet Creeper
Family

The stems are branched, woody
climbers and sometimes reach a
height or lateral length of 20-40 feet.
The leaf blades are divided into 7-11
leaflets that are toothed, oval, and
½-2 inches long. The flowers are in
clusters of 2-9. Each flower is scarlet
red, tubular, five-lobed, slightly
irregular, and 2-3 inches long. The
capsule fruits are spindle-like, 4-6
inches long, and almost an inch in
diameter. They occur frequently in
moist, rich soils over a wide area.
August - September.

Cercis canadensis
Red Bud
(Salad Tree, Judas Tree)
Leguminosae — Legume Family

This plant is the official state tree for Oklahoma. They are often shrubby but can reach a height of fifty feet in fertile, moist soils. The leaves have heart-shaped blades that are 2-6 inches long, as well as wide. The reddish-pink flowers are clustered on peduncles, appear slightly ahead of the leaves, and are about a half inch long. Pods are flattened and 2-3 inches long. They thrive along streams over a wide area. March -May.

Robinia hispida
Black Locust
(Honey Locust, False Acacia,
Moss Locust)
Leguminosae — Legume Family

These are shrubs that are highly
branched and 4-9 feet tall. The young
stems, leaf-stalks and flower-stalks
are very bristly. The leaves are
prinnately compound with 9-13
leaflets. Each leaflet is ovate or
oblong, smooth-margined and 1-2
inches long. The flowers are pink or
purple and ¼-½ inch long. They are
observed on low slopes in southern
and eastern counties but are
somewhat rare. May - June.

Schrankia Nuttallii
Sensitive Briar
(Sensitive Rose, Shame Vine)
Leguminosae — Legume Family

These plants are low, spreading,
branched, and very heavily armed
with hooked prickles. Their leaves are
twice divided into many small
segments that are about ¼ inch long.
Flowers are produced in globose,
compact masses, ⅔-1 inch in
diameter. These are at the tips of long
peduncles, attached in the leaf axes,
and are pink in color. Each pod is
very spiny and about two inches
long. Sensitive briars are fairly
common along roadside
embankments and fence lines. They
prefer dry prairies. May - July.

Centaurium Beyrichii
Centaury
Gentinanceae — Gentian Family

These are clustered and branched
plants that are 8-20 inches tall. The
flowers are pink, five-parted, and
about a half-inch across. Collectively
they form dome-like clusters, six to
twelve inches wide. They grow on
hillsides. April - June.

Petalostemum villosum
Silky Prairie Clover
(Hairy Prairie Clover)
Leguminosae — Legume Family

These plants are branched at the base and are 1-2 feet tall. They are densely villous or silky throughout. The leaves have very short petioles and 9-17 leaflets. The flowers are rose-purple (or rarely white) and are borne in dense spikes. These spikes are terminal, mostly clustered, cylindric and 1-4 inches long. They are most likely to be observed in the western counties of our state. June - August.

Sabatia campestre
Prairie Sabatia
(Rose-pink Sabatia)
Gentianaceae — Gentian Family

The stems are four-angled, branched
and 6-15 inches high. The leaves are
oval, without petioles and ½-1 inch
long. The flowers are solitary at the
ends of branches and peduncles. Each
flower is 1-2 inches broad and has
five pink petals. They are widely
distributed on prairies over a wide
area. May - July.

Agrostemma Githago
Corn Rose
(Corn Cockle, Mullen Pink, Crown-of-the-field)
Caryophyllaceae — Pink Family

These are erect, branching, hairy plants that are 1-3 feet tall. The leaves are sessile, erect, 2-4 inches long, and ¼ inch or less in width. The flowers are on long peduncles, 1-3 inches broad and light pink to reddish in color. The five sepals unite at the base to form a cup, but have long slender tips that spread out beyond the petals. These plants are infrequent and restricted to open hillsides of eastern counties. May - September.

Dianthus Armeria
Grass Pink
(Deptford Pink)
Caryophyllaceae — Pink Family

These are mostly smooth, erect plants that branch near the top and are 6-15 inches tall. The leaves are narrow and less than an inch long. The flowers have five pink to whitish petals with crinkled tips. These plants are restricted to a few counties in the northeastern fourth of the state. They prefer old fields or open wastelands. May - August.

Trifolium pratense
Meadow Clover
(Purple Clover, Honeysuckle Clover, Sugar Plum)
Leguminosae — Legume Family

The stems are mostly erect, branching, hairy and 1-2 feet tall. The leaf blades are divided into three segments that are ½-2 inches long and oval in form. The heads are globose and about an inch in length. Each flower is red to white and about ½ inch long. They are widely distributed throughout, except northwestern counties. April - November.

Tephrosia virginiana
Goat's Rue
(Cat Gut, Turkey Pea, Rabbit Pea, Devil's Shoestrings)
Leguminosae — Legume Family

These plants are 1-2 feet tall, sparsely branched, and covered with white, silky hairs. The leaves are divided to form 7-25 leaflets that are about an inch long and ¼ inch wide. The flowers are yellowish-purple and ½-¾ inch long in terminal, crowded racemes. The pods are slender, 1-2 inches long and hairy. These are dry-land plants, found infrequently throughout much of out state. June - July.

Coronilla varia
Crown Vetch
(Hive Vine, Axseed, Axwort)
Leguminosae — Legume Family

These plants are smooth, branched, straggling and 1-2 feet long. The flowers are irregular in form, ⅓-½ inch long, light pink and arranged in dense umbels. They grow mostly in eastern sections where they are encouraged for erosion prevention. May - August.

Cirsium undulatum
Wavy-leaved Thistle
Compositae — Composite Family

The stems are stout, branched, very leafy, and 1-3 feet tall. The leaves are lanceolate, whitish, lobed, spiny-margined, and 1-8 inches long. The heads are 1-3 inches broad, almost as high, and without rays. The flowers are purple or pink, tubular, five-lobed, and regular. They are widely distributed on plains and prairies. June - September.

Vicia sativa
Common Vetch
(Pebble Vetch, Spring Vetch, Tare)
Leguminosae — Legume Family

The stems are weak, spreading, ascending or climbing and 1-3 feet long. The leaves have 8-14, broad, blunt leaflets and a terminal, branching tendril. Each leaflet is about an inch long and a fourth of an inch wide. The flowers are single or paired in the angles of the upper leaves. Each flower is bluish-purple and about an inch long. They are widely distributed in waste places throughout the state. May - August.

Abronia fragrans
Pink Abronia
Nyctaginaceae — Four O'Clock Family

These are perennial, branching, slender plants that are 1-2 feet tall. The flowers are in compact clusters with more than 20 flowers per cluster. Each flower is almost an inch long, tubular and lavender-pink to white. They grow in deep sand of the western fourth of the state. June - August.

Phlox pilosa
**Wooly Phlox
(Downy Phlox, Prairie Phlox,
Sweet William)**
Polemoniaceae — Phlox Family

These are slender, hairy plants that
are 1-2 feet high. The leaves are
without petioles, spreading, 1-4
inches long and less than a third of
an inch in width. The flowers grow in
compact clusters at the stem tips.
Each flower is purple to white
(usually pinkish), five-parted, and
about a half inch wide. They are
widely distributed in open woods, or
on prairies, and prefer well drained
soils. April - June.

Verbena hastata
Blue Vervain
(False Vervain, Wild Hyssop)
Verbenaceae — Verbena Family

These are roughish perennials that are 3-6 feet tall. The flowers are in spikes at the tips of upper branches. Each flower is blue to pinkish-white and ¼-½ inch broad. They grow in moist fields or roadside drains, mostly in eastern counties. June - September.

Verbena bipinnatifida
Prairie Verbena
Verbenaceae — Verbena Family

These are hairy, extensively branched plants that are upright or somewhat prostrate, and reach a length of 6-18 inches. The leaf blades are divided into several lateral lobes that are ½-2 inches long. The flowers are in terminal spikes that become 2-4 inches long in fruit. Each flower is five-lobed, tubular, about a half inch wide, and purple or lilac. They prefer rocky or gravelly limestone soils and are frequent where these conditions exist. April - September.

Verbena canadensis
Large-flowered Verbena
Verbenaceae — Verbena Family

These plants are highly branched, likely to be somewhat prostrate, and are 8-20 inches long. The leaf blades are deeply cut into three or more broad, toothed segments, and are 1-3 inches long. The flowers are in spikes that are dense and short, at first, but becoming 2-4 inches long in fruit. Each flower is light pink to purple and ½-1 inch wide. The fruits are four-lobed when mature. They are widely distributed in sandstone prairies and more frequent in central or eastern counties. April - August.

Verbena pumila
Dwarf Wooly Verbena
Verbenaceae — Verbena Family

These plants are very wooly, weak-stemmed and up to a foot in length. They are highly branched. The leaves are deeply notched to completely divided and ½-1 inch long. The flowers are tubular, pink to blue and ⅛-¼ inch wide. They are in compact terminal clusters. They are found in waste places throughout. May - September.

Phlox divaricata
Wild Phlox
(Wild Blue Phlox, Wild Sweet William)
Polemoniaceae — Phlox Family

The stems are covered with short hairs. They are mostly upright and reach a height of 6-18 inches. The leaves are two at a node, 1-2 inches long and lance-like in form. The flowers are crowded at the tips of stems. Each flower contains five spreading petals which are united below into a tube about ⅗ inch long and ⅒ inch thick. The petals are blue to pink. They are somewhat infrequent throughout our eastern counties. April - June.

Linaria canadensis
Toadflax
(Blue Toadflax)
Scrophulariaceae — Figwort Family

These plants have slender, upright, branched stems, ½-4 feet tall. Their flowers are in slender, long racemes on the upright stems. Each flower is blue to pink, ¾-1 inch long, very irregular in form, and has a slender basal spur. These plants are widespread and frequent in dry, sandy, waste places. May - September.

Chilopsis linearis
Desert Willow
(Willowleaf Catalpa, Flowering
Willow, Flor de Membre)
Bignoniaceae — Trumpet Creeper
Family

These are shrubs or small trees with
rather slim trunks. Their branches are
weak and usually droop in a manner
similar to the willows. The leaves are
linear to lanceolate in form and 3-8
inches long. The flowers are pink to
purple and 1-1½ inches long. These
plants flourish in dry, sandy soil and
are found in our southwestern
counties. May - July.

Callirhoe alcaeoides
Light Poppy Mallow
Malvaceae — Mallow Family

These small herbs branch from the
base, are 8-20 inches tall, and grow
from thick, woody roots. The leaf-
blades are deeply cut or completely
divided and are 2-4 inches long. The
flowers are pink to white, about an
inch broad, and on 1-2 inch pedicels.
They are frequent and widely
distributed, especialy in dry soils.
May - August.

Tradescantia Tharpii
Tharp's Spiderwort
Commelinaceae — Spiderwort Family

These spiderworts are less than one foot tall. The stems, leaves, and even sepals of the flowers are covered with short, soft hairs. The flowers are about an inch wide and composed of three petals that are likely to be more pink than blue. They are restricted in their distribution, seemingly, to limestone soils, and sometimes grow quite profusely in rocky prairies such as we find in the Arbuckle Mountains and surrounding regions. April -August.

Gerardia fasciculata
Pink Gerardia
(Fascicled Gerardia)
Scrophulariaceae — Figwort Family

These plants are annuals that are finely-hairy and 1-4 feet tall. Their flowers are pink to purplish, irregular in form, borne in racemes and about an inch long. They inhabit waste places of a few southeastern counties. August - October.

Erodium texanum
Stork's Bill
Geraniaceae — Geranium Family

These plants are mostly decumbent and are about a foot in length. The flowers are red, about an inch broad and have five separate petals. They grow on rocky slopes of our southwestern counties. March - April.

Liatris aspera, var. intermedia
Handsome Blazing Star
Compositae — Composite Family

The stems are smooth, unbranched and 2-3 feet tall. The leaves are narrow and 1-4 inches long. The flowers are in heads that are about a half inch wide. Each flower is tubular below, five-lobed above, and pink. They grow on prairies throughout Eastern Oklahoma. August -September.

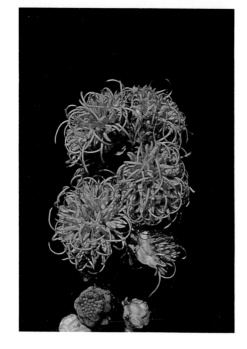

Desmodium paniculatum
**Panicled Trefoil
(Tick Trefoil)**
Leguminosae — Legume Family

These are slender, erect plants that
are 2-4 feet tall. The flowers are
irregular in form, pink to purple and
about a fourth inch long. They grow
in dry soil of hillsides in the eastern
two-thirds of the state. July -
September.

Vicia dasycarpa
**Smooth Vetch
(Cow Vetch, Cat Pea, Bird Vetch,
Smooth Tare)**
Leguminosae — Legume Family

The stems are freely branched
reaching considerable length. The leaf
blades are divided into 10-20 leaflets
and a branching tendril. The purplish
flowers are 10-30 in number in each
raceme and each is ½-1 inch long.
They have become widespread,
escaping from cultivation. They
thrive along roadsides throughout
Oklahoma. May - September.

Liatris pycnostachya
Prairie Button Snakeroot
Compositae — Composite Family

The stems are stiff-hairy above, very leafy and 2-5 feet tall. The leaves are very narrow, the lower as much as a foot long, and the upper 1-4 inches long. The heads of flowers are crowded on upper stems, ⅓-½ inch long and 3-6 flowered. The individual flowers are all similar, purple and have five lobes. They are fairly numerous in most of the eastern half of our state. August - September.

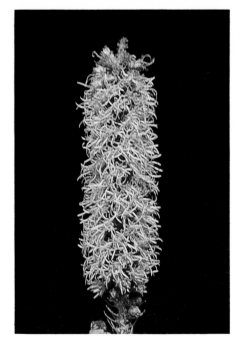

Rosa setigera
**Wild Rose
(Prairie Rose, Climbing Rose,
Rose Blush)**
Rosaceae — Rose Family

These are climbing, prickly plants
with stems several feet long. The
leaves have blades divided into three
leaflets that are 1-3 inches long and
sharply toothed. Flowers are rose
color to white and 2-3 inches wide.
Fruits are globose, reddish when
mature, and up to ½ inch in
diameter. May - July.

Krameria secundiflora
Prairie Bur
(Mexican Krameria, Linear-leaved Krameria)
Leguminosae — Legume Family

The stems are a foot or more long, branched, and prostrate. The leaves are simple, about one inch long, very narrow, and prickle-tipped. Their flowers are about one inch broad, borne singly on axillary peduncles, and purple in color. The pods are globose, hairy, spine-tipped and about ½ inch thick. They are widely distributed in prairie habitats. April - June.

Centrosema virginianum
Spurred Pea
(Spurred Butterfly Pea)
Leguminosae — Legume Family

These are perennial, climbing or trailing vines that are 2-4 feet long. The flowers are usually paired, violet, irregular in form and about two inches long. They occur in open woods of the eastern half of the state. July - August.

Dodecatheon meadia
Shooting Star
(American Cowslip, Judian Chief,
Rooster Heads, Pride-of-Ohio)
Primulaceae — Primrose Family

The stems are 1-2 feet tall and unbranched to the flower clusters. The leaves are in a basal rosette around the stem base, 3-12 inches long and ½-4 inches wide. The flowers are about an inch long, purple to white, in umbels, and with petals turned directly back toward the pedicels when mature. The capsule fruits are narrowly oval and about a half inch long. They occur in the eastern half of the state. April - May.

Rhexia mariana
Maryland Meadow Beauty
(Maryland Deer-grass)
Melastomaceae — Meadow Beauty Family

The stems are slender, sparsely branched, hairy and 1-2 feet high. The leaves are simple, short-petioled, oblong and 1-1½ inches long. The flowers are few in number on spreading pedicels at the top. Each flower is about an inch broad, with eight stamens and four pale purple petals. They grow in low moist meadows and roadside drains in a few southeastern counties. June - September.

Liatris punctata
Dotted Snakeroot
Compositae — Composite Family

The stems are unbranched, 6-30 inches high and grow in clusters from a stout rootstock. The leaves are erect, rigid, covered with tiny dots, smooth-margined, 2-6 inches long and $\frac{1}{10}$-$\frac{1}{5}$ inch wide. The heads are 3-6 flowered, $\frac{1}{2}$-$\frac{2}{3}$ inch long and crowded in long spikes. There are no ray flowers. The flowers present are purple, cylindrical, regular, five-lobed and surround by purplish plumose bristles. They seem to thrive on eroded, dry hillsides of the western two-thirds of Oklahoma. August -October.

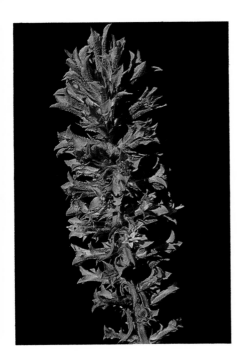

Lamium amplexicaule
Henbit
(Dead Nettle)
Labiatae — Mint Family

Liatris elegans
Elegant Blazing Star
Compositae — Composite Family

These are slender perennials that are 2-3 feet tall. The flowers are borne in small heads that are each 4-5 flowered. They are purple with bracts that are purple to white. They grow on well-drained slopes of a few of our eastern counties. August - October.

These are low, branching plants that are occasionally prostrate and 6-18 inches long. The lower leaves have petioles while upper ones have blades clasping the square stems at the nodes. The leaf blades are nearly orbicular, crinkled on the margins, and ½-1½ inches wide. The flowers are clustered in the leaf axes, purplish or red, and about a half inch long. They thrive in lawns, old fields, and waste places where moist rich soil occurs. February - October.

Vernonia Baldwinii
Baldwin Ironweed
(Purple Vernonia)
Compositae — Composite Family

The stems are stout, branched only at the top, and grow in clusters. The leaves are lanceolate, sharply toothed, 4-8 inches long, and ½-2 inches wide. The heads are 15-30 flowered and clustered on stout peduncles. The flowers are all similar and lack rays. Each flower is purple or red, tubular, regular, and has five recurved lobes. They are widely distributed on prairies and roadsides. July - September.

Mirabilis linearis
**Four O'Clock
(Umbrella-wort)**
Nyctaginaceae — Four O'Clock
Family

These plants are slender, much-branched and 3-4 feet tall. The flowers are usually in clusters of three that emerge from the same set of bracts. Each flower is pink to purple and about a half inch wide. They grow in well-drained soil throughout. June - August.

Mirabilis Nyctaginea
Heart-leaved Four O'Clock
Nyctaginaceae — Four O'Clock
Family

The stems are rather slender, mostly smooth, angled and 1-3 feet tall. The leaves are broadly ovate to lanceolate, 2-4 inches long and cordate at the base. The flower stalks are slightly hairy. Each flower is about the size of a dime and red to pink. They grow in dry soils of roadsides and old fields over a wide area. May - October.

Robinia Pseudo-Acacia
Locust Tree
(Black Locust, False Acacia)
Leguminosae — Legume Family

These are large trees that have very rough bark. Their leaves are divided to form 9-19 leaflets that are each 1-2 inches long. Flowers are in loose, drooping clusters, pinkish to white, and ½-⅝ inch long. Their pods are smooth, 2-4 inches long and about ½ inch broad. These trees are infrequent but are naturalized and continue to be transplanted around homes in our state. May - June.

Polygonum pennsylvanicum
Smartweed
(Heartweed, Lady's Thumb,
Lover's Pride, Kiss-me-over-the-
garden-gate-Kate)
Polygonaceae — Buckwheat Family

These are smooth annuals that are 1-3 feet tall. The flowers are without petals but their sepals are pink. They are borne in racemes that are spike-like. They grow in low, moist ditches or lake-margins throughout the eastern half of the state. July -September.

Oenothera speciosa
Showy Evening Primrose
(Common Evening Primrose)
Onagraceae — Evening Primrose
Family

These are much-branched plants that
are 1-3 feet tall, and occasionally
decumbent. The leaves are 2-3 inches
long and have slightly wavy margins.
The flowers are solitary in the leaf
axes, white or pink, and 1½-4 inches
wide. The capsule fruits are club-
shaped, four-ribbed and ½-¾ inch
long. They are widespread and
frequent along roadsides in open
areas. May - July.

Convolvulus arvensis
**Small Bindweed
(Hedge Bells, Corn Lily, Corn
Bind, Bear Bind)**
Convolvulaceae — Morning Glory
Family

These plants have trailing, very
slender stems, 1-3 feet long, and
sometimes unbranched. The leaves
have slender petioles and blades that
are 1-2 inches long with spreading
basal lobes which narrow to a tip.
The flowers are 1-4 on peduncles that
arise from the leaf axes. Each flower
is pink or almost white, ⅔-1 inch
broad and bell-shaped. They grow in
fields, waste places, roadsides and
lawns. They seem to occur more
frequently in the western half of
Oklahoma. May - September.

Buchnera americana
Pink Hearts
(Blue Hearts)
Scrophulariaceae — Figwort Family

These plants are slender, mostly unbranched, 1-3 feet tall and covered with short, stiff hairs. The leaves contain prominent veins and are fairly narrow with dentate margins. The flowers are borne in terminal spikes and are blue, pink, purple or white. Each flower is ½-1 inch long and about ½ inch broad when mature. They are found in sandy meadows of Eastern Oklahoma. May - August.

Claytonia virginica
Spring Beauty
(Grass Flower, Good-morning-spring)
Portulacaceae — Purslane Family

Stems are weak and there are often several from the same corm. Each stem bears only one pair of leaves. Sepals are only two but petals usually number five (rare occasions six or seven). The plant is 3-8 inches tall and often falls over before maturity. Each petal is light pink with dark pink veins. They grow in moist, open woods and among prairie grasses of meadows and pastures. They seem to be widely distributed in Oklahoma. March - May.

Oxalis violacea
Sheep Sour
(Violet Wood Sorrel, Sheep Sorrel)
Oxalidaceae — Wood-sorrel Family

These plants grow from underground
bulbs. Their stems are weak and
usually single with a branched
inflorescence. The leaves have long
petioles from the bulbs and are
divided into three leaflets that are
½-1 inch wide. The flowers are ½-1
inch wide and pink to purple. The
capsules are about an inch long when
mature. They are widely distributed
and thrive in rich sandy loam of open
woods or prairies. April - July.

Phacelia hirsuta
Hairy Phacelia
Hydrophyllaceae — Waterleaf Family

The stems branch at the base, and
along with the remainder of the plant
are very hairy. They seldom are over
a foot tall. The leaves are laterally
lobed, 1-2 inches long, and ¼-⅓ inch
wide. The flowers are in terminal,
compact racemes. Each flower is blue
to pink, five-parted, and about a half
inch wide. The capsule fruits are
globose and 4-8 seeded. They grow in
well drained soils in the eastern half
of our state. April - May.

Collinsia violacea
Narrow-leaved Collinsia
(Violet Collinsia)
Scrophulariaceae — Figwort Family

These plants have slender, erect, branched stems, and are 6-15 inches high. The flowers are solitary on peduncles from the leaf axes, as well as in clusters of 3-5 at the stem tips. Each flower is irregular in form, violet to pink, and about a half inch long. They grow in rich soils of meadows over a wide area. April - May.

Nemophila phacelioides
Baby Blue-eyes
(Woodland Nemophila)
Hydrophyllaceae — Waterleaf Family

These are hairy, branching plants that are 6-18 inches tall. Their leaves are deeply lobed laterally or divided into lateral leaflets. Each leaf is 1-3 inches long and ½-1 inch wide with 3-5 lobes on each side. The flowers are blue-lavender with pale centers, about an inch across, and single on pedicels from the leaf axes. They grow along stream banks and sandy or silty ground of meadows, in the eastern half of Oklahoma. April - May.

Lygodesmia aphylla, var. *texana*
Skeleton Weed
Compositae — Composite Family

The stems are divergently branched above, smooth and 1-2½ feet tall. The leaves are mostly basal, lance-like and deeply nothced. They are reduced to mere bracts on the upper portion. The flowering heads are large and conspicuous. Each flower is irregular in form and has a purplish ray with five teeth at the square tip. They are somewhat infrequent and only found in southwestern counties from the Arbuckle Mountains westward. May - September.

Allium canadense
Meadow Garlic
Liliaceae — Lily Family

These are bulbous plants that are up to one foot tall and often in clusters. The flowers are about ½ inch across and composed of six similar, showy perianth parts. Colors vary from pink to white. There may be as many as twenty flowers on short stalks at the tip of each stem. Occasionally ovoid bulblets replace flowers but these are without individual stalks. Commonly, these plants are seen in moist meadows over a wide range of the state. May - June.

Penstemon grandiflorus
Large-flowered Penstemon
Scrophulariaceac — Figwort Family

These Plants have rigid stems and are 2-4 feet tall. All surfaces are smooth and somewhat glossy. The leaves are oval in form and have smooth margins. The flowers are loosely arranged near the stem tips. Each flower is lavender-blue, irregular in form and nearly two inches long. They are found in the western counties and thrive best on prairie slopes. May - July.

Penstemon Buckleyi
Buckley's Penstemon
Scrophulariaceae — Figwort Family

The stems are smooth, mostly unbranched and 8-18 inches high. The leaves are lance-like, without stalks and 2-4 inches long. The flowers are numerous and mostly three at each upper stem node. Each flower has a tubular, irregular, five-lobed corolla that is strongly two-lipped. They are light lavender to white. These plants are fairly frequent in sand hills of Western Oklahoma. May - June.

Penstemon Cobaea
Cobea Beard Tongue
Scrophulariaceae — Figwort Family

These are sparingly branched, stout plants that are 1-2 feet tall. Their leaf blades are oval, toothed, rigid, and 3-5 inches long. The flowers are 1-5 at each node on the upper stems. Each flower is reddish to light purple, five-lobed, slightly irregular, tubular, and about two inches long. They occur over a wide area and seem to thrive on dry prairies, including places where topsoils have eroded away. May - July.

Monarda Russeliana
Russell's Horse Mint
Labiatae — Mint Family

The stems are square, slender, mostly unbranched and 1-2 feet tall. The leaves are paired at the stem nodes, have very short stalks and blades that are toothed with length of 2-3½ inches. Flowers are clustered at the tips of the stem. Each flower is tubular, irregular in form, pink to white and about an inch long. They are frequent in dry fields and woodlands of Eastern Oklahoma. May - July.

Monarda fistulosa
**Wild Bergamot
(Oswego Tea, Bee Balm)**
Labiatae — Mint Family

These plants are slender perennials
that are usually branched and slightly
hairy. Their leaves are 1-4 inches
long, ½-2½ inches wide at the base
and tapered to a point terminally.
Their margins are serrate. The
flowers are in clusters at the tips of
the stems. They are very irregular in
form and vary in coloration from
yellowish-pink to lilac or purple.
They grow on hillsides in much of the
eastern half of Oklahoma. June -Sept.

Phlox longipilosa
Mountain Phlox
Polemoniaceae — Phlox Family

These plants are covered by long, silky hairs. They are 1-2 feet tall and only slightly branched. The leaves are narrow and 1-3 inches in length. The flowers are borne in compact clusters at the stem tips. They are usually deep purple in color with five diverging petals that are broad enough that they overlap near the corolla tube. They are presently seen only in the western portion of the Wichita Mountains. May - July.

Scutellaria Drummondii
Annual Skullcap
Labiatae — Mint Family

These little plants differ from most other "skullcaps" by their very small flowers (not over a sixth inch long) and the presence of mostly unbranched stems from annual taproots. They are mostly western on open slopes. April - June.

Scutellaria parvula
Small Skullcap
Labiatae — Mint Family

The stems are square, extensively
branched at the base, and 3-12 inches
tall. The leaf blades are bluntly
toothed, nearly oval in form, and ⅛-1
inch long. The flowers are very
irregular in form, solitary in the leaf
axes, violet, and ⅙-⅓ inch long.
They thrive on hillsides, roadsides or
other open areas, and are more
frequent in the southwestern counties.
April - July.

Aster patens
Late Purple Aster
Compositae — Composite Family

The stems are slender, rough, 1-3 feet tall and divergently branched. The leaves are thick, somewhat rigid, clasping at the base and 1-3 inches long, below, but very small near the flowers. The flowering heads are about an inch wide, with 15-25 purplish rays. They grow in dry, open places. August - October.

Aster dumosus
Bushy Aster
(Rice-button Aster)
Compositae — Composite Family

These plants are smooth throughout, rather stiff, strongly branched and 1-3 feet tall. The leaves are narrow, rigid, smooth-margined and 1-3 inches long, except for those of the flowering branches. These are very small. The numerous heads are about ½ inch broad, borne at the tips of wiry branches at the summit and have 15-30 blue, lavender or white rays. They are found in sandy regions of the eastern counties. August - October.

Aster paludosus
Swamp Aster
Compositae — Composite Family

These plants have rough, slender stems and are 1-2½ feet tall. The flowers are borne in compact heads at the ends of the stems. Each head is 1-2 inches wide with yellow to brown disk flowers and 20-30 deep violet ray flowers, about an inch long. They grow in swampy areas of the southeastern counties. August - October.

Aster exilis
Slim Aster
Compositae — Composite Family

The stems are slender, with spreading branches, and 6-24 inches tall. The leaves are very narrow, smooth-edged, and 1-4 inches long. The flowers are in heads at the tips of the spreading branches. The rays are purplish and about a sixth inch long. The central disk flowers are tubular, five-lobed, regular, and yellow when young. They are widely distributed in moist meadows, pastures, and lawns. August - October.

Astragalus Lindheimeri
Lindheimer Pea
Leguminosae — Legume Family

The stems branch and spread out near the ground. Leaves are pinnately divided with 15-25 leaflets that are ¼-½ inch in length. The flowers are ½-1 inch long, purple, in compact racemes, and on 1-2 inch peduncles arising from leaf axes. The pods are ½-1 inch long and ¼-1 inch thick. They grow on rocky or gravelly well-drained hills and slopes in southwestern counties. April - May.

Prunella caroliniana
Heal All
Labiatae — Mint Family

These are mostly erect, but occasionally prostrate plants, with square stems and a length of 2-20 inches. The leaf blades are oval, toothed or smooth, and 1-4 inches long. The flowers are in dense terminal spikes that are 2-4 inches long in fruit. Each flower is violet, purple, or white, and ⅓-½ inch long. They are very widely distributed and thrive in fields, woods and waste places. May - October.

Astragalus missouriensis
Missouri Milk Vetch
Leguminosae — Legume Family

These plants branch from the base, have silky, gray hairs, and are 2-5 inches tall. The flower are irregular in form, violet-purple and ½-¾ inch long. They grow in meadows of well-drained soil in the southwestern part of the state. May - July.

Psoralea cuspidata
Large-bracted Psoralea
Leguminosae — Legume Family

These are mostly weak-stemmed plant that reach a length of 1-2 feet. The stems and leaves are finely hairy. Each leaf blade is divided into five leaflets that are 1-2 inches long and ⅓-½ inch wide. The flowers are in oblong, dense spikes. Each flower is bluish and almost an inch long. They thrive on rocky, prairie hillsides of the eastern and central counties. May -June.

Lobelia siphilitica
Great Lobelia
(Blue Cardinal Flower, High Belia)
Campanulaceae — Bell-flower Family

The stems are rather stout, leafy, usually unbranched, and 1-3 feet high. The flowers are compact in terminal racemes. Each flower is bright blue, tubular, five-lobed, irregular, and about an inch long. They are mostly restricted to our eastern counties and prefer moist, rich meadows. July - October.

Astragalus crassicarpus, var. *crassicarpus*
Buffalo Bean
(Ground Plum, Buffalo Apple, Buffalo Pea)
Leguminosae — Legume Family

These plants are very hairy, branched at the base and 6-15 inches tall. The flowers are purplish, ½-¾ inch long, irregular in form and borne in racemes. They grow on prairies, mostly western in the state. April -June.

Dyschoriste linearis
Dyschoriste
Acanthaceae — Acanthus Family

The stems are hairy, branched and
6-15 inches tall. The leaves are hairy,
narrow and ½-2 inches long. The
flowers are borne on very short
stalks, mostly solitary in upper leaf
angles. Each flower has five united
petals, is almost regular in form, light
purple and ½-1 inch long. They seem
to be restricted to Cotton County,
Love County and possibly a few
others, preferring dry prairies. May
-July.

Aster lateriflorus
Calico Aster
(Starved Aster, Rosemary)
Compositae — Composite Family

These plants are nearly smooth,
slender, divergently branched and 1-5
feet tall. The leaves are lanceolate,
2-5 inches long and have serrate
margins. The flowering heads are
slightly less than ½ inch broad with
yellow to purple disk flowers and
rays that are white or pale purple.
They grow in a variety of soils of
slopes and low meadows of Eastern
Oklahoma. August - October.

Asclepias purpurascens
Purple Milkweed
Asclepiadaceae — Milkweed Family

These plants have mostly
unbranched, smooth stems that are
2-4 feet high. The leaves grow all the
way to the top of the stems and are
3-8 inches long. The flowers are
borne in umbels from several of the
upper leaf axils. Each flower is deep
purple and a little smaller than a
dime. They occur in dry fields and
meadows or open woods in a few
eastern counties. June - August.

Eupatorium coelestinum
**Blue Boneset
(Mist Flower)**
Compositae — Composite Family

The stems are branched and 1-3 feet
tall. The leaf blades are broadly
ovate, toothed, 1-3 inches long and
¾-1½ inches wide. The heads are
very numerous, and ⅛-¼ inch high
as well as broad. They have no rays.
The flowers are blue, tubular with
five lobes, regular and very small.
They are widely distributed and very
frequent at the margins of lakes or
ponds. August - October.

Lespedeza intermedia
Bush Clover
Leguminosae — Legume Family

These are sparingly branched plants
that are 1-3 feet tall. The flowers
have blue to pink petals and are ⅛-¼
inch long. They grow in dry soil
throughout the eastern half of the
state. August - September.

Echinacea pallida
Pale Purple Coneflower
Compositae — Composite Family

The stems are covered with short,
stiff hairs, unbranched, and 2-3 feet
tall. The leaves are long-lanceolate,
smooth-edged, rough-hairy, and 3-8
inches long. The heads are about
three-fourths of an inch in diameter
and only at the stem tips. The rays
are long, drooping, rose-purple or
occasionally pale, 1-3 inches long,
and ⅛-¼ inch wide. The central disk
flowers are rigid-tipped. They are
infrequent on hillsides of central and
eastern counties. May - July.

Tragopogon porrifolius
Purple Goat's Beard
**(Oyster Plant, Purple Salsify, Nap-
at-noon, Jerusalem Star)**
Compositae — Composite Family

These plants are very similar to the
Yellow Goat's Beard (page 127). The
distinguishing feature is primarily the
purple color of the flowers of this
species. They grow in waste places of
towns and cities, as well as
occasionally along the roadsides.
April - August.

— 75 —

Asclepias speciosa
Showy Milkweed
Asclepiadaceae — Milkweed Family

The stems are simple, stout, pale and
1-2½ feet tall. The leaves are simple,
broadly oval and 3-8 inches long. The
flowers are in umbels (usually several
at upper nodes). Each flower is
purple-green and ⅓-½ inch long. The
fruits are follicles that are 3-4 inches
long and densely wooly. They are
widely distributed in moist soil of
open areas. May - July.

Pluchea purpurascens
Marsh Fleabane
Compositae — Composite Family

These plants are stiff annuals that reach a height of 2-4 feet. The leaves are sessile, lanceolate or elliptic, toothed, and hairy beneath. Their flowers are pink to purple and are in small, compact heads enclosed basally by purplish to green involucral bracts (phyllaries). They grow along the shorelines of some of Oklahoma's larger lakes. July - Sept.

Eryngium Leavenworthii
**Leavenworth's Eryngo
(Pineapple Thistle)**
Umbelliferae — Carrot Family

These are stout plants that are
branched above and resemble thistles.
The leaves are divided into spiny-
toothed segments. Flowers are in
heads that are purplish to pink,
oblong, 1-2 inches long, and about ¾
inch thick. They thrive in dry, open,
uplands, and are mostly eastern in
our state. July - October.

Monarda citriodora
Lemon Monarda
(Prairie Bergamot, Horse Mint)
Labiatae — Mint Family

These are square-stemmed, mostly
unbranched plants that are 1-2 feet
high. Their leaves are toothed,
simple, 1-3 inches long, and ⅙-½
inch wide. The flowers are in dense
clusters, both terminal and at the
upper nodes. Each flower cluster is
subtended by a group of bracts which
are grayish-green. Each individual
flower is irregular in form, pink to
purple or nearly white, and ⅔-1 inch
long. They are widely distributed and
thrive on dry plains. June
-September.

Eustoma grandiflorum
Bluebell
**(Russell's Eustoma, Large-
flowered Eustoma)**
Gentianaceae — Gentian Family

These are erect, stout, sparingly
branched plants, that are 1-3 feet tall.
Their leaves are 1-3 inches long, ½-2
inches wide, have smooth edges, and
lack petioles. The flowers grow on
peduncles that attach singly in the
upper leaf axes. Each flower is 2-3
inches broad, purple, and mostly
five-parted. They occur in rich soils
of meadows, prairies, and roadsides
throughout. May - August.

Solanum elaegnifolium
Silvery Nightshade
Solanaceae — Nightshade Family

These plants are highly branched, silvery-hairy all over, 1-3 feet tall, and armed with slender, sharp prickles. Their leaf blades are oblong, fairly smooth on the edges, 1-4 inches long, and ¼-1 inch wide. The flowers are in axillary racemes. Each flower is five-lobed, violet or blue, and ⅔-1 inch broad. Their fruits are globular berries that are ¼-½ inch in diameter, smooth, and yellow when ripe. They are frequent in waste places, especially in the western half of the state. May - September.

Hydrolea ovata
Hydrolea
Hydrophyllaceae — Waterleaf Family

The stems are erect, branched at the top, hairy and 1-3 feet tall. There is usually a small spine in each leaf angle. The leaves have short petioles and simple blades that are smooth-edged, oval and 1-2½ inches long. The flowers contain five united petals that are separated at the tips. They are pink to purple and in compact clusters. They grow in moist, low areas of several of our eastern counties. May - September.

Solanum carolinense
Common Sticker Weed
(Horse Nettle, Sand Briar, Apple-of-Sodom, Carolina Nightshade)
Solanaceae — Nightshade Family

These are stout, branched plants, that are 1-4 feet tall, and armed with stout, yellow prickles. The leaf blades are laterally lobed, 2-6 inches long, and ½-2 inches wide. Flowers are in racemes which grow at the tips of peduncles that attach in the leaf axes. Each flower is five-lobed purplish, and 1-1½ inches wide. The fruits are globular berries that are about three-fourths of an inch in diameter, smooth, and orange-yellow when ripe. They are frequent in fields and waste places throughout. May -September.

Erythronium albidum
Dog-tooth Lily
Liliaceae — Lily Family

The plants are about six to eight inches tall with flowers of six similar perianth parts that are up to two inches across if spread laterally. However, they often recurve as they mature. The color of the flower varies from lavender to pink. They are more numerous in the eastern half of Oklahoma. March - May.

Tradescantia ohiensis
Ohio Spiderwort
Commelinaceae — Spiderwort Family

These spiderworts are quite attractive and can be observed over a broad segment of the state during the summer months. They seem to thrive best on disturbed sandy loams of fields and roadsides. Their stems are erect, smooth and unbranched. Leaves are thick, 8-12 inches long and less than an inch in width. Flowers cluster at the stem tips and emerge in a series from bracts. Each flower contains three blue to pink petals. Many attempts have been made to transplant these plants to flower gardens with only minimal success. May - August.

Baptisia australis
Blue Wild Indigo
Leguminosae — Legume Family

These are smooth, stout plants, 4-6
feet tall. Their leaf blades are divided
into three leaflets that are long-oval,
have smooth margins, and are 1-3
inches long. Flowers are in terminal
racemes 6-12 inches long. Each flower
is dark blue, irregular, and ¾ inch
long. The pods are 1-2 inches long,
about ½ inch thick, and sharp-
pointed at the tips. They thrive in
rich prairie soils throughout. May -
July.

Passiflora incarnata
Passion Flower
(Passion Vine, Maypop Vine)
Passifloraceae — Passion-flower
Family

These plants are vines that climb to a
height of 10-30 feet. The leaves are
3-lobed and 3-5 inches broad. The
leaf margins are finely toothed. The
flowers grow singly on stalks from
leaf angles. Each flower is about two
inches broad and white or purple
with a pink or purple crown. They
grow along fences or among small
trees in our eastern counties. May -
July.

Nemastylis geminiflora
Northern Nemastylis
Iridaceae — Iris Family

These are weak-stemmed plants
growing from bulbs that are
sometimes a foot underground. They
are 1-2 feet tall with leaves that are
grass-like and extend beyond the
flowers. The latter are in pairs or
solitary from paired bracts at the
stem tips. Each flower is about two
inches broad and composed of six,
very thin, blue perianth segments.
The flowers are attractive in their
natural setting, but do not retain their
beauty after collection. They prefer
prairie habitats and are widely
distributed. April - June.

Viola missouriensis
Missouri Violet
Violaceae — Violet Family

These plants are very short-stemmed
with long-petioled leaves growing
from ground level. The leaf blades
are heart-shaped, 1-4 inches wide,
and have toothed margins. The
flowers are irregular in form, violet
to light blue, and about an inch long.
They thrive in moist meadows and
low woodland creek banks. April -
May.

Anemone caroliniana, forma *violacea*
Purple Wind Flower
(Prairie Anemone)
Ranunculaceae — Buttercup Family

These are plants that are similar to the White Wind Flower (page 177) except for the color of the sepals. They grow on prairies or meadows over a wide range. April - June.

Sisyrinchium campestre
Blue-eyed Grass
Iridaceae — Iris Family

Prior to flowering, these little plants really resemble bunch grasses. They grow in compact bunches and are 6-18 inches tall. When flowers appear, they are violet to white and are about an inch in width. Each flower has six similar perianth parts and emerges from paired bracts. This is the most common blue-eyed grass in Oklahoma and is seen along roadsides over most of the state. It thrives best in open areas. May -July.

Physalis lobata
Purple-flowered Ground Cherry
Solanaceae — Nightshade Family

These are low-growing, mostly prostrate plants, that are 6-12 inches long. The leaf blades are broadly oval, wavy-margined or lobed, and 1-3 inches long. The flowers are on 1-2 inch peduncles that are solitary in the leaf axes. Each flower is bell-like, purplish, and about an inch broad. The berry fruits are similar to green cherries in appearance and are enclosed within green, inflated, five-angled envelopes. They grow on high plains and are frequent along our highways. May - September.

Lupinus texensis
Bluebonnet
(Texas Lupine)
Leguminosae — Legume Family

These are annuals that are up to two feet tall and covered with hairs. The flowers are blue with some white parts, about a half inch long and produced in racemes. They grow in most of our southern counties, especially along highways, where they have spread from seeding. April - May.

Androstephium coeruleum
Androstephium
Liliaceae — Lily Family

Most members of the lily family have bulbs but these little plants grow from corms. They are about six inches tall and produce an umbel of two to seven flowers at the tip of each stem. The lower half of the perianth of each flower is funnel-like and it branches into six similar perianth lobes that are light blue to purplish in color. Each flower is about one inch across. They are distributed over a good portion of Oklahoma, especially in high prairie habitats. April - June.

Evolvulus Nuttallianus
Wooly Evolvulus
Convolvulaceae — Morning Glory Family

These are gray-silky perennials that are 3-9 inches tall. The flowers are funnel-like, purple or blue and up to ½ inch broad. They grow on dry plains throughout. May - July.

Salvia azurea, var. *grandiflora*
**Large-Flowered Blue Sage
(Pitcher's Sage, Tall Sage)**
Labiatae — Mint Family

These are square-stemmed, stout, simple or branched plants that grow to a height of 2-5 feet. The leaves are mostly smooth-margined, 2-5 inches long, and ⅙-⅔ inch wide. The flowers are in clusters attached to upper nodes. Each flower is blue or occasionally white, irregular in form, and about an inch long. They are widely distributed in approximately the eastern two-thirds of the state in dry soils. July - September.

Veronica polita
**Blue Speedwell
(Corn Speedwell, Wall Speedwell)**
Scrophulariaceae — Figwort Family

The stems are hairy, slender, branched when more mature, mostly spreading near the ground and 3-10 inches long. The leaves are hairy, toothed on the margins and ⅕-½ inch long. The flowers are borne singly in the leaf angles. Each one is only about ¹⁄₁₀ inch wide, light blue, with four slightly unequal petals that are united most of their length. They thrive along walkways in parks or in private lawns as well as waste places along our roadways. February - November.

Amsonia ciliata, var. *texana*
Blue Star
Apocynaceae — Dogbane Family

These are mostly non-branched plants
that are 2-4 feet tall and in bunches.
The leaves are lance-like, 2-4 inches
long, ½-2 inches wide and smooth-
edged. The flowers are blue, five-
parted, ¾-1 inch wide, and in
clusters at the tops of the plants. The
follicle fruits are paired, 2-4 inches
long, and a sixth inch thick. They
prefer moist soils of prairies and
meadows. April - July.

Commelina erecta
Slender Day-flower
Commelinaceae — Spiderwort Family

These little day-flower plants have
very weak stems that may be as much
as two feet tall, but only grow
upward when supported by other
plants. The leaves are 3-6 inches long
and less than 1 inch wide. Flowers are
no more than 1 inch across, clustered,
pale blue and emerge from small
green bracts. Each flower contains
three petals but one is reduced in size.
They may be observed intermittently
across most of Oklahoma. July -
October.

Ipomoea hederacea, var. *integriuscula*
Blue Morning Glory
Convolvulaceae — Morning Glory
Family

These are twining annuals with
deeply cordate leaves that are
unlobed and 2-4 inches long. The
bell-shaped flowers are light blue
when young but become more purple
with maturity. They are borne on
very short stalks, or occasionally
seem to be sessile on their stems.
These plants grow in old fields or
along roadsides where plenty of
moisture is available. They are more
abundant in eastern counties. July -
October.

Camassia scilloides
Wild Hyacinth
(Eastern Camass)
Liliaceae — Lily Family

These are slender plants that grow from bulbs and on occasion may reach a height of as much as three feet. Flowers grow in racemes that are three to twelve inches long. Each flower is about one inch across, composed of six similar perianth segments, and blue, or occasionally white. Colonies of these hyacinths can often be observed along roadsides and meadows, especially in low moist soils. They are more numerous in eastern and southern counties. April - June.

Delphinium carolinianum
Carolina Larkspur
(Blue Larkspur, Azure Larkspur)
Ranunculaceae — Buttercup Family

These plants are slender, covered with short hairs and 1-2 feet tall. The flowers are blue, irregular in form, about an inch long and borne in loose racemes. They grow on prairies of the eastern half of our state. May - July.

Centaurea Cyanus
**Bachelor's Button
(Blue Bottle, Corn Bottle,
Brushes, Blue Caps)**
Compositae — Composite Family

The stems are wooly, at least when
young, slender, branched and 1-3 feet
tall. The leaves are simple, slender
and 3-6 inches long. Flowers are in
heads that are 1-2 inches broad, on
long peduncles. The flowers are all
regular, five-lobed and vary in color
from purple to white. They have
escaped from gardens and may occur
in any part of the state. May
-September.

Triodanis perfoliata
Common Venus Looking-glass
Campanulaceae — Bell-flower Family

The stems are densely leafy, mostly
unbranched, weak and 6-24 inches
tall. The leaves are clasping almost
circular, usually toothed, ¼-1 inch
long, and about the same width. The
flowers are 1-3 in the leaf axes. Each
one is blue or violet, has four or five
(mostly five) spreading lobes, is
regular, and ½-¾ inch broad. Each
capsule is cup-shaped and ⅙-¼ inch
long. They are widespread and fairly
frequent throughout. May
-September.

Cichorium Intybus
Chicory
(Blue Sailors, Blue Dandelion,
Wild Succory, Coffee Weed)
Compositae — Composite Family

The stems are freely branched, stiff, rough and 1-3 feet tall. The basal leaves are remotely toothed and 3-6 inches long but the upper ones are much reduced. The heads have only irregular (ligulate) flowers and are 1-1½ inches broad. The flowers are usually blue, but are occasionally white. These are escapes from gardens and occur sporadically throughout our area. June - October.

Amorpha canescens
Lead Plant
(Wild Tea, Shoestrings)
Leguminosae — Legume Family

These are bushy shrubs, 1-3 feet high that are white-hairy throughout, leaves are rather compact, 2-4 inches long and composed of 21-51 leaflets. Flowers are blue and in spikes of 2-7 inches in length. Each pod is single-seeded and about ¹⁄₁₀ inch in length. They grow in scattered thickets on prairies, over a wide area. June - August.

Helianthus hirsutus
Rough Sunflower
Compositae — Composite Family

The stems are densely stiff-hairy, branched above and 2-4 feet tall. The leaves have short stalks and blades that are broad at the bases but taper to the tips. Each blade is finely toothed and 3-6 inches long. The flowers are clustered in large heads. Each ray is yellow and two-lobed at the tip. Each central flower is bottle-like, five-lobed and yellow. They are fairly numerous in our eastern counties. July - October.

Helianthus laetiflorus
Oblong-leaved Sunflower
Compositae — Composite Family

The stems are stout, somewhat rough-hairy, branched above and 3-7 feet tall. The leaves are ovate-oblong, thick, toothed and 2-8 inches long. The yellow, flowering heads are numerous, 2-4 inches broad and have 12-20 rays. They thrive in sandy or gravelly meadows of several eastern counties. August - October.

Helianthus Maximiliani
Maximilian's Sunflower
Compositae — Composite Family

The stems are rough-hairy, scarcely branched, and 2-12 feet high. The leaves are narrowly lanceolate, finely toothed or smooth-edged, 3-7 inches long, and ½-1½ inches wide. The heads are 2-3 inches broad on short peduncles. The 15-30 rays are yellow, two-toothed at the tips, and ½-1 inch long. The central disk flowers are yellow, tubular, regular, and five-toothed. They are frequent inhabitants of dry prairies throughout the state. August - October.

Helianthus mollis
Hairy Sunflower
Compositae — Composite Family

The stems are stout, densely hairy,
sparingly branched, and 2-4 feet high.
The leaves are 2-5 inches long, ovate
to lanceolate, lack petioles, and have
toothed margins. The heads are
solitary or few, and 2-3 inches broad.
The 15-25 rays are yellow, two-
toothed, and about an inch long. The
central disk flowers are yellow,
regular, tubular, and five-toothed.
They are widely distributed in
wastelands. August - September.

Helianthus annuus
**Common Sunflower
(Comb Flower, Larea Bell, Golden Bell)**
Compositae — Composite Family

The stems are rough-hairy, branched above, and 3-6 feet high. The leaf blades are broadly ovate, toothed, 3-12 inches long, and 1-6 inches wide. The heads are 3-6 inches wide and at the stem tips. The rays are bright yellow, undivided at the tips, and 1-1½ inches long. The disk flowers are purple or brown, tubular, regular, and five-toothed. They are the most widely distributed as well as the most frequent of our sunflowers. July -September.

Helianthus petiolaris
Prairie Sunflower
Compositae — Composite Family

The stems are densely stiff-hairy,
much branched and 1-3 feet tall. The
leaves have petioles that are up to
three inches long and blades that are
1-3 inches long. The flowers are of
two types in compact heads. The
outer ones are irregular and have
long yellow rays. The central flowers
are bottle-like, five-lobed and brown.
They are quite numerous in
southwestern Oklahoma, especially
in sandy wastelands. June -
September.

Berlandiera texana
**Texas Berlandiera
(Green Eyes)**
Compositae — Composite Family

The stems are erect, rough, branched
and 2-3 feet tall. The leaves are dark
green, toothed, broad and 2-4 inches
long. The flowers are of two kinds in
compact heads. The ray flowers are
tubular, irregular and have rays that
are two-lobed at their tips. The
central flowers are tubular, regular
and brown. They are widely
distributed in mostly sandstone
prairies. July - August.

Bidens aristosa
Western Tickseed
Compositae — Composite Family

These are mostly annuals that are 1-3 feet tall and highly branched. The flowers are in heads that are 1-2 inches broad with 6-9 yellow rays. They grow in wet places in several of our eastern counties. August - October.

Engelmannia pinnatifida
Cut-leaved Daisy
Compositae — Composite Family

The stems are usually branched above and 1-3 feet tall. The basal leaves have slender petioles and blades that are deeply cut into large lobes. The upper leaves have no petioles and are not so deeply cut. The heads are numerous and about an inch broad. The rays are yellow, three-toothed, and about a half inch long. The central disk flowers are tubular, regular, five-lobed and five-toothed. They are normally seen in southern and western counties. May - August.

Silphium integrifolium
Tall Rosinweed
Compositae — Composite Family

These plants are usually stiff-hairy, branched near the top and 3-6 feet tall. The heads have broad, basal bracts and 18-30 yellow rays that are each about an inch long. They grow on prairies and along fences of the eastern half of the state. June - September.

Coreopsis lanceolata
Large-flowered Tickseed
Compositae — Composite Family

The stems are usually branched above and 1-3 feet tall. The leaves are mostly divided into leaflets that are oblong and 1-3 inches long. The heads are on long peduncles and are 1-2 inches broad. The 6-10 rays are yellow, four-lobed, and about ¾ inch long. The central disk flowers are yellow, tubular, regular, and five-toothed. They are mostly restricted to prairies and plains of the eastern half of the state. May - August.

Chrysopsis villosa, var. *canescens*
Silver Golden Aster
(Hairy Golden Aster, Rosin Weed)
Compositae — Composite Family

These plants are much branched, covered with gray hairs and about a foot tall. The flowering heads have bright yellow ray flowers as well as disk flowers. The entire head is 1-1½ inches wide. They grow in dry soils of the western half of the state. June - August.

Chrysopsis pilosa
Golden Aster
Compositae — Composite Family

The stems are densely hairy, branched above, and 1-2 feet tall. The leaves are lanceolate, smooth-edged, 1-3 inches long, and ⅙-½ inch wide. The heads are few at the ends of branches and ⅔-1 inch broad. The rays are yellow and about a third inch long. The central disk flowers are yellow, tubular, five-toothed, and regular. They are widely distributed and grow in sandy waste lands. July -August.

Verbesina encelioides
Golden Crownbeard
Compositae — Composite Family

The stems are densely gray-hairy, much branched and 1-2 feet high. The leaves are broadly lance-like, coarsely toothed, gray-hairy and 2-4 inches long. The leaf stalks are winged on both sides. The flowering heads contain 12-15 rays that are bright yellow, 3-toothed and about an inch long. Their central flowers are bottle-like, yellow and numerous. These plants prefer deep sandy soil of open wastelands. June - October.

Helenium tenuifolium
Fine-leaved Sneezeweed
Compositae — Composite Family

The stems are profusely branched and 8-24 inches high. The leaves are numerous, very slender, and ½-2 inches long. The heads are numerous and ¾-1¼ inches thick. The 4-8 rays are yellow, drooping, 3-4 toothed and about a half inch long. The central flowers form most of the globose disk, are yellow, regular, cylindrical, and five-toothed. They are well distributed over most of the state. August - October.

Haplopappus ciliatus
Wax Goldenweed
(Clasping-leaved Haplopappus)
Compositae — Composite Family

These plants are erect, glabrous and 2-5 feet tall. They are mostly unbranched to near the top. The alternate leaves are sessile, oval and very sharply toothed. The heads are few and clustered at the ends of the branches. The rays as well as the disk flowers are yellow. They grow throughout most of the state but are most numerous in prairie habitats. July - September.

Haplopappus phyllocephalus
Showy Haplopappus
Compositae — Composite Family

The stems are only slightly branched, smooth and 2-3 feet tall. The leaves are finely-toothed, 1-2 inches long and ¼-½ inch wide. The flowers are of two types, but all are yellow. The ray flowers are irregular and lack notches or lobes at the tips. The central flowers are bottle-like, regular and five-lobed at the tips. They are infrequent throughout. May - July.

Hymenoxys scaposa
Prairie Hymenoxys
Compositae — Composite Family

The stems are branched at the base from woody roots, and are 3-8 inches high. The leaves are very narrow and 1-2 inches long. The heads are on long peduncles and ⅔-1 inch broad. The rays are orange-yellow, three-toothed, and about an inch long. They are found in our western counties in dry rocky places. May -September.

Grindelia squarrosa
Broad-leaved Gum Plant
Compositae — Composite Family

The stems are branched and 10-24 inches high. The leaves are oblong or oval, toothed with sharp points, ½-2 inches long, and ¼-½ inch wide. The heads are 1-1¼ inches broad and waxy. The rays are up to an inch long, yellow and not toothed at the tips. The disk flowers are tubular, yellow, regular, and five-lobed. They are widely distributed in dry prairie soils. June - September.

Senecio glabellus
Butterweed
(Cress-leaved Groundsel)
Compositae — Composite Family

These are smooth annuals that are 6-24 inches tall. The heads are composed of ray flowers and disk flowers. All flowers are yellow. They grow in poorly drained areas and are widely distributed in the eastern half of the state. April - August.

Senecio plattensis
Prairie Ragwort
Compositae — Composite Family

The stems are branched only at the tops and seldom over 1½ feet high. The leaves are oval or oblong in outline and toothed only, or toothed and lobed. The heads are numerous and about a half inch broad. The rays are yellow, three-toothed and ½-¾ inch long. The disk flowers are yellow, tubular, regular, and five-toothed. They grow on prairies and in open woods throughout. April - June.

Gaillardia pinnatifida
Cut-leaved Gaillardia
(Yellow Gaillardia)
Compositae — Composite Family

Three species of Gaillardia were included in the 1976 "Roadside Flowers of Oklahoma." This one differs from those three by its laterally-lobed leaves. The rays are yellow and the disk flowers are reddish-brown. They grow in western Oklahoma. April - June.

Gaillardia serotinum
Yellow Gaillardia
Compositae — Composite Family

The stems are mostly branched, short-hairy and 1-2 feet tall. The stem leaves lack petioles, are lanceolate, toothed and 1-2 inches long. The heads are about two inches broad and on long peduncles. The rays are 8-12 in number, three-lobed and light yellow. The disk flowers are regular, five-lobed and reddish-brown. They are found in scattered stands in dry open woods, fields, or roadsides. July - September.

Thelesperma filifolium
Thread-leaved Thelesperma
Compositae — Composite Family

The stems are branched and 1-3 feet
high. The leaves are divided into
thread-like segments that are ⅓-1
inch long. The several heads are on
long, slender peduncles and are about
an inch broad. The rays are yellow,
three-toothed, and ½-1 inch long.
The disk flowers are brownish-tipped,
tubular, regular, and five-toothed.
They are frequent in dry prairie soils
throughout. June - August.

Coreopsis tinctoria
Golden Coreopsis
(Wild Flax, Garden Tickseed)
Compositae — Composite Family

The stems are branched and 1-4 feet tall. The leaf blades are once or twice divided into leaflets that are very narrow. The heads are numerous, about an inch broad, and have brownish inner bracts. The rays are yellow with brown bases, three-lobed at the tips, and about a half inch long. The central disk flowers are yellow to brownish, tubular, regular, and five-toothed. They are widespread and prefer low wet places. May - September.

Helenium amarum, var. *badium*

Sneezeweed
(Yellow Star)

Compositae — Composite Family

The stems are profusely branched and 8-24 inches tall. The flowers are in heads. Each ray flower is yellow but the disk flowers ar reddish-brown (the way in which they differ from the Sneezeweed of the 1976 publication). They are widely distributed in the southwestern fourth of Oklahoma. April - August.

Ratibida columnifera, forma
pulcherrima
Mexican Hat
(Long-headed Coneflower, Prairie
Coneflower)
Compositae — Composite Family

These plants are very similar to the
"Prairie Coneflower" of the 1976
publication. This form has the
purplish-brown color near the base of
the rays. This makes them more
colorful. They grow on prairies and
meadows over a wide area. May -
August.

Rudbeckia grandiflora
Large-flowered Coneflower
Compositae — Composite Family

The stems are mostly unbranched,
rough and 2-3 feet tall. The leaves are
largely near the base, rough, toothed
and have blades that are 2-6 inches
long. The flowers are in compact
heads at the stem tips and are of two
types. Each outer flower is yellow
with a flattened corolla section that is
ray-like, two-toothed at its tip and
drooping. Each central flower is
bottle-like and yellow, changing to
brown. They grow on dry prairies in
our southeastern counties. June -
August.

Rudbeckia hirta, var. *pulcherrima*
**Black-eyed Susan
(Brown-eyed Susan, Yellow Daisy,
Brown Betty, Poor-land Daisy)**
Compositae — Composite Family

The stems are very hairy, sparingly
branched, and 1-3 feet high. The
leaves are very hairy, sparingly
tooth-edged or smooth, 2-7 inches
long, and ½-2 inches wide. The
heads are solitary or few, and 2-4
inches broad. The rays are orange to
yellow, 10-20 in number and 1-2
inches long. The central disk flowers
are purple-brown, tubular, regular
and five-toothed. They abound in
disturbed soils of prairies and plains
throughout our state. May - July.

Rudbeckia amplexicaulis
Clasping-leaved Coneflower
Compositae — Composite Family

The stems are smooth, glossy, branched, and 1-2 feet tall. The leaves are smooth-margined, clasp the stems at the bases, and are 1-4 inches long. The heads are solitary at the ends of branches and about two inches broad. The rays are yellow, four-toothed, and 1-2 inches long. The central disks are ovoid to oblong, often an inch high, and brownish. They grow in moist soils throughout. June - August.

Lindheimera texana
Texas Star Daisy
Compositae — Composite Family

The stems are branched and 6-24
inches tall. The leaves are densely
clustered on young stems, remotely
toothed, hairy, 1-4 inches long and
¼-1 inch wide. The heads are at tips
of peduncles from upper leaf axes and
¼-½ inch broad. The 5 rays are
yellow, 2 or 3-toothed, and ¾-1 inch
long. The disk flowers are yellow,
tubular, regular and five-toothed.
They grow in clay or sandy fields and
on roadsides of our southwesten
counties. March - May.

Psilostrophe villosa
Plains Psilostrophe
Compositae — Composite Family

These are branched perennials that
are covered with loose, white
wooliness and are 6-24 inches tall.
The disk flowers and ray flowers are
lemon-yellow, and are in heads that
are ⅓-½ inch broad. They grow in
sandy prairies of the western half of
the state. May - September.

Gutierrezia dracunculoides
Broom Weed
Compositae — Composite Family

The stems are slender, much branched, smooth and 6-18 inches high. The leaves are ½-2 inches long and less than ¼ inch wide. The heads are solitary at the ends of short branches, about ¼ inch high and have 10-30 flowers. The yellow rays are about ¼ inch long and rounded at the tips. The central disk flowers are yellow, very small and mostly lack seeds. They are very frequent on prairies throughout the state. September - October.

Zinnia grandiflora
Prairie Zinnia
Compositae — Composite Family

These are perennials that are much
branched and reach a height of 4-6
inches. The flowers are in heads that
each has four or five, broad, yellow
rays. They grow in dry soils of a few
of our western counties. June -
September.

Solidago speciosa, var. *angustata*
Noble Goldenrod
(Showy Goldenrod)
Compositae — Composite Family

These are stout plants that are 3-7 feet tall. The yellow heads of flowers are ¼-½ inch broad and about the same length. These heads are very abundant at the upper stem tips. They are mostly restricted to the northeastern fourth of the state but are occasionally seen as far south as the Arbuckle Mountains. August - October.

Solidago rigida
Stiff Goldenrod
(Hard-leaved Goldenrod)
Compositae — Composite Family

These plants have stout stems that are unbranched except near the flowering region. There are short, stiff hairs over most of the leaf and stem surface. The leaves are ovate to oblong, rounded at the base and 1-2 inches long. The flowers are yellow and are contained in small heads which are very numerous on the upper branches. These goldenrods grow in dry, sandy, gravelly or rocky soil in a high percentage of our counties. August - September.

Solidago nitida
Smooth Goldenrod
Compositae — Composite Family

The stems are smooth to the touch, rigid, unbranched to near the inflorescence, slender and 1-3 feet high. The leaves are narrow, smooth, thick and 1-3 inches long. The yellow heads are about ¼ inch high with a small number of tiny flowers. They grow throughout the southeast ¼ of the state. August - September.

Solidago missouriensis
Missouri Goldenrod
Compositae — Composite Family

The stems are smooth, rather slender, and 2-4 feet high. The leaves are slender, narrowed at the base, rough-margined and 2-4 inches long. The flowering heads are numerous, yellow-flowered and ⅙-¼ inch high. Each head has 6-13 short rays. They are widely distributed on dry prairies. July - October.

Solidago nemoralis
Field Goldenrod (Gray Goldenrod, Dwarf Goldenrod)
Compositae — Composite Family

These plants are slender, ashy-gray, hairy and 6-24 inches tall. The leaves are thick, rigid and 3-6 inches long below but much smaller near the inflorescence. The heads are borne along the upper side of the upper stem branches and are about ¼ inch high. They thrive in dry soils of old fields and roadsides and are widely distributed. July - November.

Solidago radula
Western Rough Goldenrod
Compositae — Composite Family

The stems are rather slender, rough, hairy and 1-3 feet tall. The leaves are thick, rough on both sides, oblanceolate, and 3-8 inches long below but very small near the flowers. The yellow heads are about ¼ inch high and occupy only the upper side of long, spreading floral branches. There are only 3-7 small rays on each head. These goldenrods grow in well-drained soil in the eastern half of the state. August - October.

Krigia Dandelion
**Dwarf Dandelion
(Dwarf Goatsbeard)**
Compositae — Composite Family

The stems are extremely short and unbranched. The leaves are clustered around the short stem. The heads are about an inch broad and on long solitary peduncles. The flowers are orange to yellow, ray-like, five-toothed, and about a half inch long. They grow throughout. April - June.

Taraxacum officinale
**Common Dandelion
(Blowball, Irish Daisy, Milk Witch,
Puff Ball, Yellow Gowan)**
Compositae — Composite Family

The stems are extremely short with leaf clusters at ground level. The leaves are deeply and irregularly notched, 3-10 inches long, and ½-2 inches wide. The heads are developed near the basal leaves and are 1-2 inches broad. After fruiting the peduncles elongate to a height of 2-18 inches. The flowers are all ray flowers. Each ray is yellow, five-toothed and ¼-½ inch long. They are very frequent weeds of lawns and fields throughout. January -December.

Lactuca canadensis, var. *latifolia*
Wild Lettuce
(Tall Lettuce, Trumpet Weed, Fire Weed, Devil's Weed)
Compositae — Composite Family

These plants are slender, 3-10 feet tall and much branched near the top. The flowering heads are pale yellow and about a half inch wide. They very noticeably fold in during afternoons of sunny days so that they are hidden by their bracts. They are widely distributed in moist meadows or roadsides. June - November.

Pyrrhopappus scaposus
False Dandelion
Compositae — Composite Family

These plants have their leaves clustered at the base of 1-2 feet stems. This differs from the False Dandelion of the 1976 publication since their leaves are on upper stems as well as the base. The flowers are all yellow and irregular in form. They grow on prairies of mostly the western half of the state. April - June.

Oenothera laciniata
Cut-leaved Evening Primrose
Onagraceae — Evening Primrose
Family

These are simple or sparingly
branched plants that are 4-30 inches
tall and may be more or less
prostrate. The leaves are deeply
pinnately cut and are 1-2 inches long.
Their flowers are very pale yellow,
on peduncles in the leaf axes, and are
½-1½ inches broad. The capsules are
1-2 inches long and about a tenth
inch thick. They prefer dry sandy
waste lands on prairies or plains.
May - June.

Tragopogon major
Yellow Goat's Beard
(Meadow Salsify, Noontide,
Joseph's Flower, Buck's Beard,
Go-to-bed-at-noon)
Compositae — Composite Family

The stems are branched near the top,
smooth and 1-3 feet high. The leaves
are long and tapered to a point at the
tip, but broad at the base. The heads
have all irregular flowers. Their
flattend portions are yellow, five-
toothed at the tip and blunt, or
square-tipped. Each head has several
bracts which extend well beyond the
yellow floral parts. The fruiting
structures contain parachute-like
fibers that are similar in structure to
those of the dandelion but they are
much larger. They are increasing in
frequency but are mostly restricted to
waste places of the western half of
our state. June - October.

Cirsium horridulum
Yellow Thistle
Compositae — Composite Family

The stems are smooth when mature, branched, thick and 2-5 feet tall. The leaves are quite abundant, have many spine-tipped lobes and are 2-5 inches long. The flowers are many in compact heads at the upper stem tips. Each flower is slender, yellow to purplish, regular and five-lobed. The entire head is 2-4 inches broad and 1-3 inches high. They grow in sandy soil of our southeastern counties. May - August.

Oenothera laciniata, var. *grandiflora*
Sand Primrose
Onagraceae — Evening Primrose
Family

These plants are similar in stem and
leaf structure to the more widely
distributed "Cutleaf Evening
Primrose." However, the flowers of
this variety are much larger (2-3
inches broad) and more golden
yellow in color. They grow in sand of
western counties. May - July.

Oenothera rhombipetala
Four-point Evening Primrose
Onagraceae — Evening Primrose
Family

These are mostly unbranched plants
that are 2-4 feet tall. The leaf blades
are remotely sharp-toothed and 2-4
nches long. The flowers are in
terminal leafy-bracted spikes, yellow,
1-2 inches broad, and night-
blooming. Their capsules are slightly
curved, ½-⅔ inch long, and about a
tenth inch thick. They are widespread
on prairies and mostly western in
Oklahoma. June - July.

Oenothera serrulata
Tooth-leaved Evening Primrose
Onagraceae — Evening Primrose
Family

These are erect plants with relatively few branches. Their stems are often reddish, stiff, and 4-18 inches high. The leaves are 1-3 inches long, $\frac{1}{6}$-$\frac{1}{4}$ inch wide, and have remotely toothed margins. The flowers are yellow and attach in the upper leaf axes. The capsule fruits are silvery, near an inch in length, and about a tenth of an inch thick. They are common and widespread throughout. May - July.

Oenothera brachycarpa
Short-pod Primrose
(Stemless Primrose)
Onagraceae — Evening Primrose
Family

These are low, perennial plants with soft, gray, short hairs. The leaves are basal and are arranged in a rosette. Each leaf is ovate to narrowly oblong, lobed and 3-9 inches in length. Their flowers are light yellow and basally attached. When fully open each flower is about 2 or 3 inches in circumference. These little plants are somewhat rare in Oklahoma but are occasionally observed along the roadsides and open, waste areas. They are a little more numerous in the western half of the state. April - July.

Oenothera missouriensis
Missouri Evening Primrose
(Large-flowered Primrose)
Onagraceae — Evening Primrose
Family

The stems are decumbent or upright, finely hairy, and 6-12 inches long. The leaves are narrowly oval, smooth-edged or slightly toothed, 2-6 inches long and ⅙-½ inch wide. Each flower is quite showy, 3-6 inches broad and bright yellow. They grow in dry soils of prairie slopes and are widely distributed. May - July.

Ludwigia alternifolia
Rattle Box
(Seed Box)
Onagraceae — Evening Primrose
Family

These plants are mostly smooth,
branching, and 2-3 feet tall. The leaf
blades are 2-5 inches long and
without petioles. Flowers are single,
on peduncles in the leaf axes, yellow,
and ½-⅔ inch wide. The capsule
fruits are cubic and about a fifth inch
long, retaining the four sepals in
fruit. They are widespread in swamps
and margins of ponds or streams.
June - September.

Oenothera Greggii
Gregg's Buttercup
Onagraceae — Evening Primrose
Family

The stems are stout, hairy, branched
and 6-18 inches tall. The leaves are
slightly toothed and 1-2 inches long.
Flowers are borne singly in the upper
axils of their leaves. Each flower has
four bright yellow petals that are
about ½-1 inch long. The flowers are
reddish in bud. They flourish on
sandy or gravelly slopes of our
southwestern counties. May - June.

Jussiaea repens
Primrose Willow
(Water Primrose, Creeping
Primrose Willow, Clove Strip)
Onagraceae — Evening Primrose
Family

The stems are creeping or floating,
root at the nodes, and are 1-3 feet
long. The leaf blades narrow to the
base and apex, and are 1-4 inches
long. Their flowers are yellow and
½-1 inch wide. The capsule fruits
taper at the base, are smooth, 1-1½
inches long, and about an eighth inch
thick. They grow in ponds, mostly in
the eastern counties. June - August.

Erysimum asperum
Western Wall-flower
(Prairie Rocket, Orange Mustard)
Cruciferae — Mustard Family

Stems are 1-3 feet tall with little branching, except the upper portion, and stiff-hairy throughout. Leaves are oblong, slightly toothed and 1-3 inches long. Flowers are in racemes and orange-yellow in color. Each flower is up to an inch across. The fruit pods are 1-4 inches long and about $\frac{1}{12}$ inch thick. These plants are widely distributed in dry open places. May - June.

Ranunculus Harveyi
Harvey's Buttercup
Ranunculaceae — Buttercup Family

These plants have branching, smooth stems that are 6-18 inches tall. The flowers have the glossy, yellow petals that typify true buttercups. Each flower is ¾-1 inch broad with five sepals, 5 petals, several stamens and several simple pistils. They grow on dry slopes of our eastern counties. March - May.

Lesquerella gracilis
**Yellow-flowered Bladderpod
(Slender Bladderpod)**
Cruciferae — Mustard Family

Stems are slender, 10-18 inches high, and freely branching. Leaves are 1-3 inches long, and oval, with wavy margins. Flowers are in long racemes. Each flower is less than one inch long and has four yellow petals. The pods are spherical or nearly so, about ¼ inch across, and with long styles remaining attached. These little plants produce much of our roadside, yellow "carpet" in the spring. They are widespread and abundant. March - May.

Ribes odoratum
**Golden Currant
(Buffalo Currant, Missouri
Currant)**
Saxifragaceae — Saxifrage Family

These are smooth shrubs that are 3-5
feet tall. The flowers are yellow,
tubular, ½-1 inch long, and borne in
leafy-bracted racemes. They grow
along streams or in roadside ditches
in most of the state. March - May.

Linum sulcatum
Yellow Flax
Linaceae — Flax Family

These are annuals that branch at the
stem tips and are 1-2 feet tall. The
flowers are regular in form, lose their
petals quickly and are about a half
inch broad. They grow in rich, well-
drained meadows over a wide area.
May - August.

Linum rigidum, var. *Berlandieri*
Prairie Flax
(Large-flowered Yellow Flax)
Linaceae — Flax Family

These plants are branched, stiff, and 6-18 inches tall. Their leaves are erect, ⅓-1 inch long and ¹⁄₂₀-¹⁄₁₀ inch wide. The flowers are bright yellow, with a tinge of orange near the center, and about an inch wide. The fruits are ovoid capsules that are about ⅕ inch long. They are prairie plants and are widespread. April -August.

Hypericum sphaerocarpum
Round-pod St. John's-wort
Hypericaceae — St. John's-wort
Family

The stems are only slightly branched, upright and 1-3 feet tall. The leaves are simple, without petioles, oblong and 1-3 inches long. The plants are smooth throughout. The flowers are clustered at the top, and have many stamens as well as five yellow petals. They are numerous on rocky slopes and low places of southern counties. June - September.

Hypericum perforatum
Rosin Rose
(Common St. John's-wort, Touch-and-heal, Amber, Penny John)
Hypericaceae — St. John's-wort
Family

These plants are wiry perennials that are much branched and 1-2 feet tall. The flowers are yellow with a slight coppery cast, ⅔-1 inch broad and numerous on tips of upper branches. They grow in fields and on roadsides and are restricted to a few of our northeastern counties. May - August.

Rhynchosia latifolius
Prairie Rhynchosia
Leguminosae — Legume Family

The stems are trailing or climbing, softly hairy and sometimes 5 feet long. The leaves have three, broad leaflets. The flowers are in racemes that may be almost a foot long when fully mature. Each flower is about an inch long with pale-yellow petals that barely exceed the sepals. They grow on dry plains. May - June.

Hypoxis hirsuta
**Yellow Star-grass
(Star-of-Bethlehem)**
Amaryllidaceae — Amaryllis Family

Their leaves are grass-like but they are obviously not true grasses as they have perianth parts. The latter are yellow inside, all alike, and make up flowers which are about ½ inch in diameter. Each plant grows from a corm, is 2-6 inches tall and bears its flowers in 2-6 flowered umbels (or rarely single-flowered). These plants are widely distributed in eastern Oklahoma but are not usually seen in great numbers in any section. They thrive in open woods and dry prairies. May - October.

Opuntia compressa
Prickly Pear
Cactaceae — Cactus Family

These are prostrate, prickly plants with flattened joints that are each deep green and 2-5 inches long. Their spines are 1-4 together and ½-1 inch long. Flowers are yellow, often with reddish center, and 2-4 inches broad. The fruits are club-shaped, smooth, fleshy, and 1-2 inches long. They grow in dry sandy or rocky soils, mostly western. May - August.

Mentzelia oligosperma
Stickleaf
(Few-seeded Mentzelia)
Loasaceae — Loasa Family

These plants are covered with short, stiff hairs and are 1-3 feet tall. The leaves are ovate, coarsely toothed, 1-3 inches long and mostly sessile. Their flowers are yellow, ½-1 inch broad and have five petals. May -July.

Cucurbita foetidissima
Common Gourd
(Wild Pumpkin, Missouri Gourd, Calabazilla)
Cucurbitaceae — Gourd Family

The stems are stout, bristly and spreading to a length of 15-25 feet. The leaves are almost triangular, thick, finely toothed, and 4-13 inches long. The flowers are of two kinds, some having three stamens, others have a pitil, regular, and 2½-4 inches long. The fruits are globular, green striped, and 2-3 inches in diameter. They are widely distributed in waste places that are well-drained. May - September.

Verbascum Blattaria
Moth Mullen
Scrophulariaceae — Figwort Family

The stems are erect, slender, mostly
smooth and 2-6 feet tall. The leaves
are mostly without petioles, taper to
the tips and vary from near a foot
long at the base to less than an inch
on upper portions. The flowers have
united petals with five yellow to
white lobes and are about an inch
wide. They thrive in open areas
throughout the eastern one-third of
our state. May - November.

Gerardia pectinata
Yellow Gerardia
Scrophulariaceae — Figwort Family

These plants are annuals that are
finely hairy and 1-4 feet tall. The
flowers are irregular in form, yellow
and produced in the axils of upper
leaves. They grow on gravelly
hillsides in the eastern half of the
state. August - October.

Pedicularis canadensis
Lousewort
(Snaffles, High Heal-all,
Beefsteak Plant)
Scrophulariaceae — Figwort Family

These are hairy perennials that are 6-18 inches tall with leaves that are laterally lobed. The flowers are light yellow, irregular, ½-¾ inch long and borne in spikes. They grow in dry woods and are mostly in the eastern half of the state. April - June.

Castilleja citrina
Yellow Paint Brush
Scrophulariaceae — Figwort Family

These plants branch profusely at the base and are 6-15 inches tall. Their leaves are deeply cut to form 3-5, long, slender, lateral lobes, and are 1-2 inches long. The upper leaves, near the inflorescence, are yellow-tipped. The flowers are in compact, terminal clusters and are obscured by the colorful upper leaves. They are fairly common in occurrence on dry prairies of our southwestern counties. May - July.

Potentilla recta
Rought-fruited Cinquefoil
Rosaceae — Rose Family

The stems are rather stout, hairy, erect, much-branched, and 1-2 feet tall. The leaves have 5-7 leaflets. Each leaflet is 1-3 inches long and noticeably toothed on the edges. The flowers are numerous, on spreading stalks, light yellow and ½-¾ inch wide. They are numerous on the roadsides of the eastern half of our state. June - September.

Nelumbo lutea
Water Lily
(Yellow Nelumbo, Pond Nut,
Wonkapin, American Lotus)
Nymphaeaceae — Water Lily Family

Stems are weak and submerged in
water while leaf blades and flowers
emerge above the surface. The leaf
blades are disk-like or nearly so and
the leaf petioles are attached near the
middle of these blades. The flowers
are solitary at the stem tips, yellow,
and 4-10 inches across. They are
easily identified but not so very
numerous in Oklahoma. They grow
in shallow waters of ponds, lakes,
and streams. July - August.

Baptisia nuttalliana
Nuttall's Baptisia
Leguminosae — Legume Family

These are upright plants with
spreading branches. The entire plant
often is canopy-like, as broad as three
feet and reaches a height of two to
three feet. The leaves have three
leaflets and each leaflet is oval with
remotely toothed margins. The
flowers are cream to yellow and ¾-1
inch long. They are found in
scattered communities throughout the
eastern counties. May - July.

Baptisia sphaerocarpa
Golden Wild Indigo
(Yellow Baptisia)
Leguminosae — Legume Family

These plants are smooth, stout, and
2-4 feet tall, with very little
branching. The leaf blades are
divided into three leaflets that are
oblong, 1-3 inches long, and have
smooth margins. The flowers are in
an upright terminal inflorescence, 1-2
feet long. They are irregularly
shaped, golden-yellow in color, and
about an inch long. The pods are
oval to oblong and about an inch
long. They occur very sporadically
but are widely distributed in prairies
and meadows. April - June.

Petalostemum aurea
**Golden Petalostemum
(Golden Dalea)**
Leguminosae — Legume Family

The stems are erect, simple, and 1-2 feet tall. Each leaf is composed of 5-9 leaflets that are not over one-half inch long. Spikes are solitary at stem tips, 1-3 inches long and ½-¾ inch thick. The flowers are irregular, yellow and about one-third inch long. They are widely distributed in prairies and waste grounds. June -July.

Cassia fasciculata
Partridge Pea
Leguminosae — Legume Family

These plants are widely branched, erect, slender-stemmed, and 1-3 feet tall. The leaves are divided into 16-30 leaflets and are 1-3 inches long. The flowers are produced 2-3, on peduncles, arising from the leaf axes. Each flower is regular in form, 1-2 inches wide and has five yellow petals. They grow in dry soils over a very wide range. June - September.

Corydalis micrantha
**Small Corydalis
(Scrambled Eggs)**
Fumariaceae — Fumewort Family

These are weak-stemmed plants.
When flowers are observed closely,
we notice they are not more than a
half inch long. The capsules are less
than one half inch long and smooth
They are more likely to appear in
eastern counties than western and
thrive in sandy-loam prairies. March
- April.

Lithospermum incisum
**Narrow-leaved Puccoon
(Yellow Puccoon)**
Boraginaceae — Borage Family

These are wooly and branched plants that are 6-24 inches tall. The leaves are ½-2 inches long and ⅛-⅕ inch wide. The flowers are bright yellow, tubular, about an inch long, five-lobed, and with crinkled margins. They are clustered in the upper leaf axes. The fruits develop into four nutlets that are white, smooth, shining, and oval. They flourish on prairies and are very frequent throughout. April - July.

Solanum rostratum
**Buffalo Bur
(Sand Bur, Prickly Nightshade,
Texas Nettle, Prickly Potato)**
Solanaceae — Nightshade Family

These plants are highly branched, 1-2½ feet tall and strongly covered all over with slender, sharp prickles. Their leaf blades are oval, irregularly lobed laterally, or completely divided into leaflets, and are 2-5 inches long. The flowers are in axillary racemes. Each flower is five-lobed, yellow, and about an inch broad. The fruits are enclosed within prickly envelopes that are ⅓-½ inch in diameter. They are widespread on prairies. May -September.

Hoffmanseggia densiflora
Mesquite Weed
Leguminosae — Legume Family

The stems are sparsely branched,
covered with glandular, short hairs
and ½-1 foot tall. The leaves are
twice divided into leaflets that are
⅙-¼ inch long. The flowers are
crowded in terminal racemes. Each
flower is brownish-yellow and about
a half inch long. They are commonly
seen on dry compact roadsides of
most western (especially
southwestern) counties. April - July.

Polytaenia Nuttallii
Prairie Parsley
(Nuttall's Parsley)
Umbelliferae — Carrot Family

These are branching, stout plants that are 1-3 feet tall. Their leaves are deeply notched or divided and each larger segment is 1-3 inches long. The flowers are in compound umbels and are fairly conspicuous in the tops of the plants. Each flower is yellow, about a sixth inch wide, and supported by a short pedicel. The fruits are smooth, oval, flattened, and about a fourth inch long. These plants are restricted almost completely to prairies of eastern Oklahoma. May - July.

Lomatium foeniculaceum
Hairy Parsley
(Meadow Parsley, Carrot-leaved Parsley)
Umbelliferae — Carrot Family

These are stemless plants with long taproots. The leaves are very finely divided into small segments. Flowers grow in compound umbels attached at the tips of 3-8 inch peduncles that exceed the leaves in height. Each flower is very small and yellow. The fruits are oval, about a fourth inch long, and have lateral wings. They inhabit dry soils of high plains. April - May.

Rumex altissimus
Tall Dock
(Pale Dock, Peach-leaved Dock)
Polygonaceae — Buckwheat Family

These plants are perennials, unbranched, stout, pale green and 2-4 feet tall. The flowers are without petals, greenish, about $\frac{1}{10}$ inch long, winged in fruit and borne in whorls on the upper stems. They change to a brown color when mature. They grow in poorly drained regions throughout. April - June.

Physalis hederaefolia var. *comata*
Hillside Ground Cherry
Solanaceae — Nightshade Family

These plants are perennial, hairy and 6-18 inches tall. The flowers are bell-shaped, yellow with a brown center, and $\frac{1}{2}$-$\frac{3}{4}$ inch broad. They grow on dry slopes over a wide area of the state. July - September.

Lonicera japonica
**Japanese Honeysuckle
(Chinese Honeysuckle)**
Caprifoliaceae — Honeysuckle Family

The stems are covered with short hairs and climbing or trailing. The leaves have short petioles and blades that are smooth-edged, broad and 1-3 inches long. The flowers are paired in the upper leaf angles, light pink, fading to yellow and 1½-3 inches long. Each flower is tubular for about a half of its length, then separates into two widely spreading or recurving lobes. They have become well established after escaping from cultivation, mostly in our eastern counties. June - August.

Caesalpinia Gillieshii
Bird-of-Paradise
Leguminosae — Legume Family

These are shrubs that are 3-12 feet tall and have leaves with many oval leaflets. The flowers have yellowish petals and extremely long, red stamens. This plant is often cultivated but has in recent years been collected in several locations along the roadsides of southwestern counties. It seems to grow best in sandy soils. May - July.

Hibiscus militaris
**Rose Mallow
(Sweating Weed, Halberd-leaved
Rose)**
Malvaceae — Mallow Family

The plants are 3-5 feet tall and
smooth throughout. The leaf blades
are toothed, 4-5 inches long and with
broad bases that are sometimes lobed.
The leaf petioles are 1-6 inches long.
The flowers have five pink petals,
darker centers and are 2-3 inches
long. They grow along rivers and
other low places. July - September.

Hymenocallis occidentalis
Spider Lily
Amaryllidaceae — Amaryllis Family

These are large-stemmed plants that grow from bulbs and reach a height of 3-4 feet. The flowers are white with six stamens that are attached to a funnel-form crown. Each flower is 3-5 inches wide and they are arranged in umbels. They grow in marshes of McCurtain County. May - July.

Sagittaria platyphylla
Ovate-leaved Arrowhead
Alismataceae — Water Plantain
Family

The arrowheads are found in shallow
water of many ponds and lakes
throughout Oklahoma. Their stems
are perennial but weak, usually
branched and up to 4 feet tall. The
flowers are in clusters of three at the
tip of each stem branch. Each flower
has three petals that fall early. July -
September.

Sagittaria latifolia
Duck Potato
Alismataceae — Water Plantain
Family

These are smooth and unbranched
plants that are 1-4 feet tall. The
leaves have long, thick petioles and
blades that are ovate and most likely
sagittate. The lobes of the blades may
be as long as the main body. The
flowers are about an inch broad and
are white. They are widely
distributed in the state and are found
in shallow ponds or margins of lakes.
June - September.

Nymphaea odorata
**Water Nymph
(Water Lily, Pond Lily, Water
Cabbage)**
Nymphaeaceae — Water Lily Family

These are weak-stemmed plants with
floating leaves. Each leaf blade is 4-12
inches in diameter and basally cleft.
The flowers are mostly floating and
white or occasionally pink. The
petals, stamens and pistils are
numerous on a fleshy receptacle.
They prefer ponds or sluggish streams
and are widely distributed. June
-September.

Argemone intermedia
Prickly Poppy
(Leafy Prickly Poppy)
Papaveraceae — Poppy Family

The stems are stout, prickly, and about two feet tall. The leaves are light green, spine-tipped at the irregular edges, and vary from one inch length above to several inches below. Their flowers are 3-4 inches wide, white, and almost sessile on the stem tips. They have three spine-tipped sepals which are lost early. These plants are widely distributed on prairies and plains. May - August.

Aphanostephus skirrobasis
Lazy Daisy
Compositae — Composite Family

These plants are erect or diffusely
branched and 6-24 inches high.
Flowers are in heads, having outer
rays that are white, numerous, and
about a half inch long. The central
flowers are numerous and yellow.
They thrive on very dry, rocky or
gravelly prairies, and are somewhat
infrequent throughout. May - August.

Chrysanthemum Leucanthemum
Ox-eye Daisy
(White Daisy, Moon Daisy, Field
Daisy, Poverty Plant)
Compositae — Composite Family

The stems are mostly unbranched,
smooth and 1-3 feet tall. The leaves
are toothed or deeply cut, without
petioles and 1-3 inches long. The
heads are solitary or only few on
long peduncles. The 20-30 rays are
white while the disk flowers are light
yellow. They are fairly abundant in
the northeastern counties. May
-November.

Echinacea angustifolia
Narrow-leaved Coneflower
Compositae — Composite Family

The stems are covered with short,
stiff hairs, usually unbranched, and
1-2 feet tall. The leaves are mostly
lanceolate, smooth-edged, 3-8 inches
long, and ⅓-1 inch wide. The heads
are about an inch wide and only at
the stem tips. The 12-20 rays are
purple, crimson, or rarely pale, and
spreading or drooping with three
terminal teeth. They are infrequent
throughout. June - October.

Erigeron strigosus
White Top
(Daisy Fleabane)
Compositae — Composite Family

These plants are 1-4 feet tall, covered
with short hairs and branched only
near the tip. Each flowering head is
about a half inch broad with many
yellow, disk flowers and numerous
narrow, white (ocassionally pink
tinged) rays. They grow in fields and
waste places and are widely
distributed. May - November.

Elephantopus carolinianus
Elephant's Foot
Compositae — Composite Family

The stems are broadly branched
above and 1-3 feet tall. The flowers
are loose in the heads and surrounded
by large leafy bracts. There are no
ray flowers. The flowers present are
tubular, regular, five-lobed, purple to
blue, and ¼-½ inch long. They grow
in moist places of low woods in the
eastern half. August - September.

Achillea lanulosa
Wooly Yarrow
Compositae — Composite Family

The stems are densely silky
throughout and 1-3 feet tall. The
leaves are much divided into small
segments. The lower ones have
petioles and the upper lack petioles.
The flowers are in numerous small
compact heads that are about a half
inch wide. Each head has 4-6 ray
flowers that are white, and 5-15 disk
flowers that are bottle-like. They are
widely distributed and numerous on
prairies. May - October.

Melampodium leucanthum
Rock Daisy
(Plains Melampodium)
Compositae — Composite Family

The stems are strongly branched from a woody base and 4-12 inches tall. The leaves are narrowy lanceolate, smooth-margined, grayish, hairy, 1-2 inches long, and ⅛-¼ inch wide. The heads are ½-¾ inch broad on 1-3 inch slender peduncles. The 5-9 rays are white, 2-3 toothed, and about an inch long. The central disk flowers are whitish-yellow, tubular, regular and five-toothed. They grow on dry prairies and hillsides of the western half of the state. June - October.

Euphorbia marginata
**Snow-on-the-mountain
(White-margined Spurge,
Variegated Spurge)**
Euphorbiaceae — Spurge Family

The stems are rather stout and 1-4
feet tall. The leaves are alternately
arranged, except the whorl below the
inflorescence, 1-3½ inches long, and
½-2 inches wide. The flowers are
small, without petals, but having
white petal-like appendages. The
most striking features of these plants
are the white-margined leaves that
surround the flowers. They are
widely distributed on prairies. May -
October.

Townsendia exscapa
Silky Townsendia
(Low Townsendia)
Compositae — Composite Family

These plants are practically stemless
with deep taproots. The flowers are
in heads that are 1-1½ inches wide.
The central flowers appear to be
yellow because of prominent anthers
and the rays are white or purple-
tinged. They grow on rocky, dry
slopes of the southwest. March -
June.

Gaura Lindheimeri
Large-flowered Gaura
(Wild Honeysuckle, Lindheimer
Gaura)
Onagraceae — Evening Primrose
Family

The stems have few, rigid branches
that are spreading in habit. They
reach heights of 2-5 feet. The leaves
are small and lanceolate, being much
reduced on the upper branches. The
flowers have four white to pink petals
that are about a third of an inch
long. There are eight stamens and a
style with four lobes. These plants are
widely distributed on prairie waste
lands. May - July.

Euphorbia bicolor
White-bracted Spurge
Euphorbiaceae — Spurge Family

The stems are stout, branched and 1-4 feet tall. The leaves are oval to oblong and 1-4 inches long. The upper leaves (bracts) have white margins, which cause the plants to be very conspicuous. The flowers are in cups that have white appendages. Each fruiting capsule is 3-lobed and 3-seeded. They grow in south central counties and prefer old fields and prairie roadsides. June - October.

Cnidoscolus texanus
Bull Nettle
(Spurge Nettle, Tread Softly)
Euphorbiaceae — Spurge Family

These are sturdy, branched, pale green plants that are covered with stinging hairs, and are 1-5 feet tall. The leaf blades are deeply lobed and 2-4 inches wide. The flowers lack petals but have five sepals that are united except at the tips. Each flower is white and ⅔-1½ inches broad. These plants are restricted to deep sand, and thrive very well where such is available. April - August.

Datura Metel
Large-flowered Thorn Apple
(Entire-leaved Thorn Apple)
Solanaceae — Nightshade Family

The stems are stout, branched and 4-8 feet long. They usually spread laterally and do not reach a height of more than four feet. The leaves are gray, smooth-edged, with petioles that are 1-3 inches long and blades 4-10 inches long. The flowers are solitary on short stalks in the leaf angles, white, tubular, regular and 6-7 inches long. The fruiting capsules are 1-1½ inches in diameter, almost spherical and very prickly. They grow infrequently, throughout, in waste places. July - September.

Datura Stramonium
Jimson Weed
(Thorn Apple, Jamestown Weed)
Solanaceae — Nightshade Family

The stems are branched, green to purple, and 1-6 feet tall. The leaf blades are oval in outline with several sharply tipped lobes, and 3-8 inches long. The flowers are in the leaf axes, white to purplish, tubular, about four inches long, and two inches broad. The capsule fruits are densely prickled and about two inches long. They grow in fields and waste places throughout. A very frequent location is the vicinity of barnyards or feed lots. June - September.

Ipomoea pandurata
Wild Potato Vine
(Wild Jalap, Scammony, Man-of-the-earth)
Convolvulaceae — Morning Glory Family

These are perennial vines, from an enormous fleshy taproot, and may reach a length of as much as twelve feet. The leaf blades are heart-shaped, 2-6 inches long and almost as wide. The flowers are 1-5 on peduncles arising in the leaf axes. Each flower is bell-like, white to pink, with purplish stripes in the throat, and 2-4 inches wide. They are widely distributed and frequent in old fields and waste places. They seem to prefer sandy loam where the taproots can penetrate extensively. May - September.

Clematis dioscoreifolia
Virgin's Bower
(Love Vine, Devil's Hair)
Ranunculaceae — Buttercup Family

These are woody vines that reach a
length of 10 to 15 feet. The flowers
have white sepals, no petals and
many stamens. Each flower is ¾-1½
inches broad and they are borne in
loose clusters. They grow only
sporadically in low areas where they
climb over fences or shrubs. July -
September.

Linum Lewisii
Blue Flax
(Lewis' Wild Flax, Prairie Flax)
Linaceae — Flax Family

These are branching plants that are 1-2 feet tall and are clustered at the base from perennial roots. Leaves are crowded on the stems, narrowly-oblong and ¼-1½ inches long. The flowers are fragile, light blue, and 1-1½ inches wide. They grow in open areas of prairies and rocky hillsides. They seem to be most prevalent in limestone soils. April - July.

Convolvulus incanus
Hoary Bindweed
(Wild Morning Glory, Hedge Bindweed)
Convolvulaceae — Morning Glory Family

These plants are covered by short hairs. They are spreading vines that reach a length of 1-3 feet. The flowers are regular in form, funnel-like and white to rose color. They grow in waste places where soil is well drained. April - August.

Delphinium virescens
Prairie Larkspur
Ranunculaceae — Buttercup Family

Stems are stout, 1-3 feet tall, and usually unbranched. Leaves are divided into several narrow segments. The flowers grow in racemes and each one has a spur at its base. They are white to blue in color and 1-2 inches long, including the spur. These are prairie plants and are widely distributed in pastures, old fields, roadsides and meadows. May - July.

Anemonella thallictroides
May Flower
(Rue Anemone)
Ranunculaceae — Buttercup Family

These are slender annuals that are 4-9 inches tall. The flowers have no petals but have 5-10 white sepals and are ½-1 inch broad. They grow in moist woods in the eastern half of the state. April - May.

Valerianella longiflora
**Long-flowered Corn Salad
(Showy Valerianella)**
Valerianaceae — Valerian Family

The stems are several times forked
and are 6-12 inches high. The leaves
are broad and blunt at the tips, 1-3
inches long, and ⅓-⅔ inch wide. The
flowers are in compact terminal
clusters. Each flower is pink or white,
tubular, five-lobed, almost regular, a
fourth inch broad, and a half inch
long. They occur in large but
infrequent communities in moist
rocky situations. April - May.

Dithyrea Wislizenii
Spectacle Pod
Cruciferae — Mustard Family

These are greyish plants that branch
near the top and are 1-5 feet tall. The
leaf blades are broad, taper to the
tips and without petioles. The flowers
grow in terminal racemes that may be
a foot long in the fruiting stage. Each
flower has four light blue to purplish
petals. Each fruit is shaped like the
two lenses of a set of spectacles. They
are found on sandy slopes throughout
the western half of the state. May
-August.

Arenaria Drummondii
Showy Chickweed
Caryophyllaceae — Pink Family

These are small annuals that have opposite leaves and reach a height of 5-12 inches. The flowers have five white petals and are ½-¾ inch broad. They grow in low, sandy areas over most of the eastern half of the state. April - May.

Podophyllum peltatum
Mayapple
(Mandrake, Indian Apple, Hog Apple)
Berberidaceae — Barberry Family

The mayapples have stems of 1-2 feet height with one or two leaves at their tips. Usually two leaves are present and if so, a solitary flower is borne between them. The flower is about two inches broad, white, and nodding on a stout pedicel. They frquently grow in large colonies in low, moist, shaded areas of the eastern half of Oklahoma. May - June.

Lesquerella ovalifolia, var. *alba*
White Bladderpod
(Oval-leaved Bladderpod)
Cruciferae — Mustard Family

These are perennials with strongly branching stems. The leaves are mostly basal and have oval blades that are 1-2 inches long. The flowers are in racemes and have four white petals. Each flower is about ½ inch wide. The pods are spherical and about ¼ inch in diameter. These plants are especially abundant in rocky or gravelly ridges of the Wichita and Arbuckle ranges. April -June.

Anemone caroliniana, forma *caroliniana*
White Wind Flower
(White Prairie Anemone)
These are plants with mostly basal leaves and are 4-10 inches tall. The flowers are single at the stem tip and up to two inches broad. Each flower usually has a double cycle of white sepals. They grow on prairies and are more numerous in eastern sections. April - June.

Rosa multiflora
Multiflora Rose
(Miniature Rose)
Rosaceae — Rose Family

These are climbing roses that cover
many miles of fences and shrubs in
our state. Their stems have numerous
broad-based prickles. Leaves are
pinnately compound with 7 or 9
leaflets. The flowers are mostly white
and grow in clusters and great
abundance. Each one is about an inch
or occasionally as much as 1½ inches
broad. This species has escaped from
cultivation and appears to have
established itself quite well over most
of the state. April - June.

Crataegus crus-galli
Hawthorn
(Cockspur Thorn, Thorn Apple,
Red Haw)
Rosaceae — Rose Family

These are much-branched trees,
sometimes reaching a height of thirty
feet. They have numerous spines that
are 1-7 inches long. Leaves are
alternate on the stems, oval, toothed
and 1-4 inches long. The flowers have
five pinkish to white petals and are
about ¾ inch across. The fruits are
almost spherical and are greenish-red
when mature. They are widely
distributed in the eastern half of
Oklahoma. May - June (fruiting in
October).

Prunus americana
**American Wild Plum
(Horse Plum, Red Plum, Hog
Plum, Native Plum)**
Rosaceae — Rose Family

These are shrubs or small trees that
grow to a maximum height of twenty
feet. The branches have a few
scatterd thorns. The leaves are ovate,
sharply tipped, toothed and 1-3
inches long. The white flowers are in
umbels, appear before the leaves, and
are about an inch wide. They
produce globose, red or yellow fruits
about an inch or a little less in
diameter. April - May (fruits ripening
in fall).

Prunus mexicana
**Tree Plum
(Mexican Plum)**
Rosaceae — Rose Family

These are trees that reach a height of
10-20 feet. The flowers have five
white to pink petals and are about an
inch broad. They grow in open
woods, mostly near streams or on
moist slopes. March - April.

Baptisia leucophaea
Large-bracted Wild Indigo
(Yellowish False Indigo)
Leguminosae — Legume Family

These are plants with spreading and drooping, wooly branches that seldom exceed 2 feet in height. Their leaves are sessile (no petioles) or only short petiolate, and have three leaflets which are 1-3 inches long, with smooth margins. Their flowers ar in mostly lateral racemes up to one foot in length. Flowers are dirty-white to cream-color, irregular in form, about one inch long and showy. The pods are ovoid and 1-2 inches long. They are widely distributed on prairies and roadsides. April - May.

Baptisia leucantha
White Indigo
(Large Wild Indigo, White False Indigo)
Leguminosae — Legume Family

These plants are smooth, stout, branched and 2-4 feet tall. Flowers are in lateral racemes that are up to one foot long. Each flower is white, irregular, and ¾-1 inch long. The pods are about ¾ inch long. They are found in most eastern counties of Oklahoma, in rich meadows or open woods. June - July.

Petalostemum multiflora
Round-headed Prairie Clover
Leguminosae — Legume Family

These are smooth, erect plants that branch profusely and reach a height of 1-2 feet. The leaves are divided into 3-9 narrow leaflets. The flowers are in globose heads that are ¼-½ inch thick. Each flower is white and about a sixth of an inch long. They grow in old fields, roadsides or open woods of our eastern counties. June -August.

Petalostemum candida
White Prairie Clover
Leguminosae — Legume Family

These are sparingly branched plants that are 1-2 feet tall. The leaves are divided into 5-9 leaflets that are ¾-1 inch long and less than ¹⁄₁₀ inch wide. The flowers are in compact spikes that are 1-4 inches long and about one-half inch thick. The flowers are white and about three-fourths inch long. They are widespread over our plains and prairies. June - August.

Yucca glauca
**Bear Grass
(Soap Weed, Adam's Needle, Palmillo)**
Liliaceae — Lily Family

One could not fail to notice the bear grass (or yucca) plants along the roadside. They have strong stems that reach heights of 2-5 feet, and basal leaves that are rigid, sharp-tipped and 1-3 feet long. The flowers are in terminal racemes and are greenish - white. Each flower has six similar perianth parts, and is 1-3 inches in width. There are occasionally as many as twenty or more flowers on each stem. They are widely distributed in well drained soils. May - June.

Daucus Carota
**Tall Queen Ann's Lace
(Wild Carrot, Bird's Nest, Lace
Flower Parsnip)**
Umbelliferae — Carrot Family

The stems are bristly, erect, branched
and 2-3 feet tall. The leaves greatly
resemble those of the garden carrot.
The flowers are in small umbrella-like
clusters with the stalks arranged in
the manner of a larger umbrella
(compound umbel). Each flower is
less than a fourth inch wide with five
white (rarely pink) petals. The fruits
are dry, ⅛ inch long and covered
with many hooked barbs. They
flourish in fields and waste places of
eastern Oklahoma. June - September.

Cornus florida
Flowering Dogwood
(Arrow Wood, Box Wood, Nature's Mistake, White Cornell)
Cornaceae — Dogwood Family

These are small trees with spreading branches. The leaves are opposite, with oval blades that are 3-6 inches long, and petioles that are ¼-1 inch long. The flowers are in compact clusters at the stem tips. Each flower is greenish-yellow and inconspicuous, but the clusters are surrounded by four spreading, white to pinkish bracts that are each 1-2½ inches long. The fruits are oval, red, and about a half inch long. They occur throughout, along creeks and ravines. April - May.

Ruellia strepens
Smooth Wild Petunia
Acanthaceae — Acanthus Family

The stems are branched or unbranched, mostly smooth, and 1-4 feet tall. The leaves are narrowly oval, smooth-margined, and 3-6 inches long. The flowers are solitary or clustered in the leaf axes. Each flower is white to blue, tubular, five-lobed, almost regular, and 1-2 inches long. They are widely distributed and thrive in dry fields or open wooded hillsides. May - July.

Cephalanthus occidentalis
Button Bush
(Honeyball, Globe Flower)
Rubiaceae — Madder Family

These are shrubs or small trees that are 5-15 feet tall. The leaf blades are oval, smooth-edged, 3-6 inches long, and 1-3 inches wide. The flowers are in globose heads that are about an inch in diameter. Each flower is white, tubular, four-lobed, regular, and ⅓-½ inch long. They are widely distributed and are frequent in low moist areas. June - September.

Sedum pulchellum
Stonecrop
(Rock Moss, Widow's Cross)
Crassulaceae — Stonecrop Family

These little plants branch freely from the base and may be upright or prostrate. Leaves are almost cylindrical, ¼-1 inch long, and densely crowded on the stems. Flowers are in one-sided, branching spikes (cymes) and rather crowded. Each one is purple, pink, or white, has five petals, and is up to ½ inch wide. They are widely distributed on rocks or very rocky soil that is well drained. May - July.

Stenosiphon linifolius
Flax-leaved Stenosiphon
Onagraceae — Evening Primrose Family

These are long-branched plants that reach a height of 2-5 feet. The leaves are lance-like and 1-2 inches long, the upper ones, even smaller. Flowers are in spikes that are sometimes a foot long. Each flower is white and ¼-½ inch broad. The capsule fruits are oval, hairy, and ¹/₁₀-⅕ inch long. They are frequent and widespread on hills, prairies, and plains. June -August.

Penstemon tubaeflorus
Funnel Beard Tongue
(Fox Glove)
Scrophulariaceae — Figwort Family

These are smooth plants with slender
stems and are about three feet tall.
The flowers are slightly irregular in
form, white to purplish, about ¾
inch long and arranged in loose
racemes. They grow on prairies of the
northeastern fourth of the state. May
- July.

Penstemon arkansana
Arkansas Penstemon
Scrophulariaceae — Figwort Family

The stems are slightly hairy, mostly
unbranched except at flowering tips,
slender and 2-3 feet tall. The leaves
are narrow, lance-like and have
toothed margins. The flowers are
white or slightly purple-tinted,
tubular, trumpet-like, irregular with
five lobes and 1-2 inches long. These
are in loose racemes on the upper
portion of the stems. They are widely
distributed on prairies of eastern
counties. May - July.

Physotegia angustifolia
**Pink Lion's Heart
(Dragon Head)**
Labiatae — Mint Family

The stems are rather stout, mostly
unbranched, square and 1-3 feet tall.
The leaves are very narrow, finely
toothed and 1-4 inches long. The
flowers are in loose spikes toward the
tip of the stem. Each flower is white
to pink, tubular, irregular and ½-1
inch long. They grow somewhat
infrequently in low moist open areas
of the eastern counties. June -
August.

Astragalus racemosus
Milk Vetch
Leguminosae — Legume Family

These are finely hairy plants that branch from the base and are 1-2 feet tall. The flowers are irregular in form, white to ivory, about ¾ inch long and borne in racemes. They grow on well-drained slopes of the western half of the state. June - July.

BIBLIOGRAPHY

Fernald, M. L. *Gray's Manual of Botany*, 8th ed. New York: American Book Co., 1950.

Gleason, H. A. *New Britton and Brown Illustrated Flora of the Northeastern States*. 3 vols. New York: New York Botanical Garden, 1952.

Goodman, George J. *Keys to the Spring Flora of Central Oklahoma*. Norman: University of Oklahoma Duplicating Service, 1960.

Lundell, C. L. *Flora of Texas*. 3 vols. Renner, Texas: Texas Research Foundation, 1961.

McCoy, Doyle. *A Study of Flowering Plants*. Lawton, Okla.: Private Printing, 1968, revised 1976.

McCoy, Doyle. *Roadside Flowers of Oklahoma*. 2 vols. Private Printing, 1976, 1978.

McCoy, Doyle. *Roadside Wild Fruits of Oklahoma*. Norman: University of Oklahoma Press, 1980.

McCoy, Doyle. *Roadside Trees and Shrubs of Oklahoma*. Norman: University of Oklahoma Press, 1981.

Stemen, J. R.; and Myers, W. S. *Oklahoma Flora*. Oklahoma City; Harlow Publishing Co., 1937.

Steyermark, J. A. *Flora of Missouri*. Ames: Iowa State University Press, 1963.

Waterfall, U. T. *A Catalogue of the Flora of Oklahoma*. Stillwater: Oklahoma State University Research Foundation, 1952.

Waterfall, U. T. *Keys to the Flora of Oklahoma*. 5th ed. Stillwater: Oklahoma State University Bookstore, 1960.

GLOSSARY

ACHENE. A small, dry indehiscent, 1-seeded fruit.

ACUTE. Sharp, ending in a point.

ANNUAL. Living for one growing season.

ANTHER. Pollen-bearing portion of a stamen.

APETALOUS. Lacking petals.

APPRESSED. Lying flat against and pointing upward.

AQUATIC. Water-living.

AWN. A bristle-shaped appendage.

AXIL. The angle formed between two organs.

AXILLARY. In the axil.

BEAK. Firm elongated slender structure.

BERRY. A fleshy, usually several-seeded fruit.

BRACT. A structure, more or less leaf-like, commonly subtending a flower or flowering branch.

BRISTLE. A stiff hair.

BULBLET. A small bulb, sometimes borne among the flowers.

CALYX. The sepals of a flower.

CAPSULE. A dry dehiscent fruit of two or more carpels.

CLASPING. Encircling or partially so.

COMPOUND. Composed of 2 or more similar parts.

COROLLA. The petals of a flower.

DECIDUOUS. Not evergreen; lost on maturing.

DECUMBENT. Spreading or leaning toward the ground.

DENTATE. Toothed, the teeth pointing outward.

DISK. A ring-like growth in the calyx, or in Compositae, the central portion of the flowering head, bearing tubular flowers.

DISCOID. Resembling a disk.

DIVIDED. Separated to the base.

ELLIPTIC. Rounded uniformly at each end and widest at the middle.

ENTIRE. Without teeth or lobes.

FILAMENT. Stamen stalk.

FRUIT. Mature ovary.

GLOBOSE. Spherical.

HEAD. A dense cluster.

INCISED. Sharply and irregularly cut.

INFLORESCENCE. A flower cluster.

INTERNODE. The portion between 2 nodes.

LANCEOLATE. Lance-shaped; much longer than broad, and the widest portion being between the middle and the base.

LEAFLET. A single division of a compound leaf.

LOBED. Divided into or bearing lobes.

MIDRIB. Central vein of a leaf.

NODE. The region on a stem where a leaf is formed.

NUTLET. A dry half-fruit or quarter-fruit.

OBLONG. Longer than broad, and sides nearly parallel on the margins.

OBOVATE. Ovate, but with the broadest portion away from the point of attachment.

ORBICULAR. Circular in form.

OVAL. Broadly elliptic.

OVATE. Egg-shaped in outline, the broadest portion toward the point of attachment.

OVOID. Egg-shaped in outline and three dimensional.

PALMATE. Radiately lobed, divided or arranged.

PARTED. Cleft nearly to the base.

PEDICEL. The stalk of a flower.

PEDUNCLE. The stalk of an inflorescence.

PERENNIAL. Living for a period of three or more years.

PERIANTH. The calyx, or calyx and corolla collectively.

PETIOLE. The stalk of a leaf.

PINNATE. With the veins or leaflets on either side of the rachis or midrib.

PRICKLE. Thorn-like outgrowth.

PROCUMBENT. Lying on the ground.

PUBESCENT. With short, soft hairs.

RACEME. An elongated inflorescence, the flowers on stalks and opening progressively from the bottom upward.

RAY. A branch of the inflorescence (Umbelliferae) or in Compositae, the strap-like corolla of the marginal flowers.

REFLEXED. Turned downward and outward.

RHIZOME. Underground stems that are elongate and mostly slender.

RIB. A prominent vein.

SERRATE. Having sharp teeth pointing forward.

SESSILE. Without a stalk.

SIMPLE. Not compound.

SPIKE. Similar to a raceme but the flowers sessile.

STANDARD. Upper and usually largest petal of a legume flower.

TENDRIL. A slender and usually twining outgrowth.

TRIFOLIATE. With three leaflets.

TUBER. Fleshy underground stem.

TUBERCLE. Small tuber-like protuberance.

UMBEL. An inflorescence with the pedicels all arising from one point.

UMBELLATE. Resembling or having an umbel.

VEIN. A vascular strand, especially as these strands appear in leaves.

VILLOUS. Very hairy.

WING. Somewhat flattened extension. Also one of two lateral petals in legumes.

WHORL. The arrangement of leaves and other appendages when three or more are attached at a node.

Index

Composition and paste-up by Artype, Inc. Color separation, Magnacolor, and printing by Ebsco Graphics, Oklahoma City, OK.